TEREZÍN IN THE "FINAL SOLUTION OF THE JEWISH QUESTION" 1941–1945

TEREZÍN

Guide to the Permanent Exhibition of the Ghetto Museum in Terezín

PAMÁTNÍK TEREZÍN
MALÁ PEVNOST
MUZEUM GHETTA

OSWALD®

TEREZÍN IN THE "FINAL SOLUTION OF THE JEWISH QUESTION" 1941–1945

Vojtěch Blodig

TEREZÍN IN THE "FINAL SOLUTION OF THE JEWISH QUESTION" 1941–1945

CONTENTS

(1) **Entrance to the Ghetto Museum**

GHETTO MUSEUM

The very first suggestions to establish a Ghetto Museum in Terezín appeared soon after Czechoslovakia's liberation from Nazi occupation in 1945. By then the former Ghetto inmates had already proposed the foundation of a museum that would remind the future generations of the history of the Terezín Ghetto and its role in the "Final Solution of the Jewish Question", as the perpetrators of that heinous crime dubbed their plan for the extermination of European Jewry in the territories occupied by Hitler's Germany.

However, the plan to set up such a museum was first postponed, and later completely shelved due to the prevailing political developments in postwar Czechoslovakia. These reflected the overall political climate in the country and its official ideology, marked – ever since February 1948 – by thinly camouflaged anti-Semitism as one of its salient features. In its consequences, this led to attempts at suppressing and obliterating the memory of the victims of the Nazi extermination of the Jews during World War II. Ideological limits were also imposed on the activities of the Terezín Memorial, which was allowed to mark the existence of the Terezín Ghetto only quite marginally.

Fresh hopes re-emerged in 1968, when a political thaw in the then Czechoslovakia revived the plans for the establishment of a Ghetto Museum and led to short-term relaxation of the tight control on the Terezín Memorial's research and adult education activities. After the Soviet-led suppression of the "Prague Spring" pro-democracy movement in 1968, the old ideology returned to stay for quite a long time. Consequently, the long-planned museum could not be established in Terezín even though its municipal school, selected as the site for a new museum, had already been moved in the early 1970s to a new building on the outskirts of the town. Instead, "Permanent Exhibition of the History of the National Security Corps (Police) and Revolutionary Traditions of North Bohemia" was installed in the school. Its establishment, which required no small financial resources, turned out to be a typical example of the arrogance of this country's former communist rulers.

This absurd situation could be remedied only after the democratic changes unleashed in November 1989. The Terezín Memorial whose new policy prioritized the establishment of a Ghetto Museum was eventually granted the right to use the former school building for that purpose. This decision was duly supported by both the new Ministry of Culture of the Czech Republic and the Terezín Initiative, an international association incorporating the former Terezín Ghetto inmates, which had been established soon after November 1989. For its part, the Terezín Initiative took the lion's share in preparations for the construction of the Ghetto Museum, in securing financial resources for its foundation as well as in the actual project implementation. After all, the team of authors commissioned to prepare the exhibition in the nascent museum included also members of the Terezín Initiative. A similar situation prevailed ten years later during preparations for the installation of the exhibition's definitive version.

The first measure – after the Terezín Memorial assumed ownership of the building for the Museum – was to remove its costly and pretentious marble wall linings, its crystal glass chandeliers, stained glass windows and other magnificent elements that stood in stark contrast to the role this particular object played at the time of the Ghetto. As a result, restoration of the building's original simplicity was part and parcel of the overall exhibition design. Within a record time of less than a year, the Memorial succeeded in amassing exhibits, drawing up a script for the exhibition and building it in the Ghetto Museum. It was inaugurated on October 17, 1991, during the commemorative events to mark the 50th anniversary of the start of deportations of the Jewish inhabitants from the Czech lands.

The new exhibition, at that time regarded as temporary, was expected to serve for a couple of years at best, before being replaced by a definitive version. The plan was that the final exhibition would also feature some additional topics and exhibits to be obtained from the domestic and foreign archives, different institutions and individuals. But as is often the case with many other "temporary" measures, the first installation of the permanent exhibition of the Ghetto Museum proved to have a very long life indeed. What undoubtedly helped in this respect was the favorable reception the exhibition had received from experts and visitors alike. However, after several years its temporary and makeshift character began to show in various technical problems, eventually calling for the reconstruction of some of its parts. Vital repairs had to be financed from the funds provided by the Terezín Initiative Foundation, later by its successor, the Terezín Initiative Institute. These contributions facilitated preparations for the construction of a definitive exhibition and later for the installation of the first part of the permanent exhibition on the building's first (ground) floor.

During the decade that elapsed between the installation of the temporary exhibition and its definitive version, many other projects were implemented within the framework of the Terezín Memorial's exhibition program, and several permanent exhibitions, linking up and supplementing the Ghetto Museum's core display, were also staged. The first one called "Mortality and Burials in the Terezín Ghetto" was installed in the crematorium in Terezín's Jewish Cemetery. Other displays are situated on the second floor of the former Magdeburg Barracks, the wartime seat of the Jewish Self-Administration. Back in 1997, the Terezín Memorial opened a reconstructed prisoners' dormitory from the time of the Ghetto. Up to the year 2000, this was gradually followed by these permanent exhibitions: "Music in the Terezín Ghetto", "Art in the Terezín Ghetto", "Literary Work in the Terezín Ghetto" and "Theater in the Terezín Ghetto". In 2001, the Memorial opened reverently adjusted premises of the former Columbarium, complete with its reconstructed original equipment, and the Ghetto's Central Mortuary housing an exhibition entitled "The Central Mortuary and Funeral Services in the Terezín Ghetto". Since the mid-1990s visitors have been able to view the reconstructed prayer room from the time of the Ghetto situated in Dlouhá Street.

The construction of the Ghetto Museum's definitive exhibition called "Terezín in the 'Final Solution of the Jewish Question' 1941–1945" proceeded in two stages between 1999 and 2001. The first to be set up was part of the exhibition located in the two halls and the adjacent corridor on the Museum's first (ground) floor. Designed to provide the visitors with basic information on the history of Terezín and its Ghetto, this exhibition highlights in particular the fate of the Ghetto's youngest inmates who lived in that building during the war. Consequently, its entrance hall is covered with the faces of some of those children as they looked before their deportation to the Ghetto as well as photographs taken during a visit to Terezín paid by a delegation of the International Committee of the Red Cross at the end of the war. On display in the hall as well as in other first (ground) floor premises are also the world-famous drawings by children from the Terezín Ghetto. These are supplemented by examples illustrating their poems and magazine articles, exhibited in the next hall. Still, the highlight of the first part of the exhibition is the list of the names of the 8,000 children up to 15 years of age, who perished either in the Terezín Ghetto or later – after their deportation from Terezín – in the places of extermination in the East. Their names cover the walls of the second hall on the first (ground) floor.

The main historical-documentary section of the exhibition is on the second floor of the building, opened to the public on November 26, 2001, on the occasion of acts of remembrance marking the 60th anniversary of the establishment of the Terezín Ghetto. Its installation was made possible by a subsidy from the Ministry of Culture of the Czech Republic, while a major financial contribution was also granted by the Conference on Jewish Material Claims Against Germany. A linchpin connecting this part of the exhibition with the keynote subject of the Ghetto's youngest inmates, as treated on the first (ground) floor of the building, is a large collage on the staircase wall, made up of children's drawings. It is designed in a way to divide the drawings by distinct dark strips symbolizing stylized bars. The unique documentary drawings by Helga Weissová-Hošková, representing everyday life in the Ghetto as seen through children's eyes, stand in stark contrast with the drawings by different children from the Ghetto. These hark back primarily to what was their happy childhood world before their deportation to Terezín.

Situated in the adjacent corridor is the introductory section of the Memorial's historical-documentary exhibition called "Plotting Genocide". This introduces the basic tenets of the anti-Jewish ideology and the practical policies applied first in Hitler's Germany, and subsequently in the German-occupied countries. Main attention is devoted to developments in the then Protectorate of Bohemia and Moravia.

The follow-up part of the exhibition, located in the first of the three halls on this floor, is entitled "Ghetto, Later the 'Jewish Settlement Territory' – Reception and Transit Camp for Jewish Prisoners in

Terezín". Proceeding in chronological order, this section traces the history of the Ghetto, explaining its basic functions and its place in the Nazi murderous mechanism of the "Final Solution of the Jewish Question".

The second and largest of the exhibition halls on the second floor bears the title "Life and Death in Terezín – The Faces of an Ordinary Day in Ghetto Life". Its thematic blocks illustrate the characteristic features of everyday life in the Ghetto, such as signs of resistance and human solidarity, the inmates' spiritual life, their wide-ranging cultural activities aimed at reinforcing the spirit of the prisoners, their lack of space, hunger, slave labor and the struggle waged by the local medical teams to save the lives of their fellow prisoners, dying and death. Other subjects include the position of old prisoners, children and youth, introducing the communities of prisoners from different countries, the lack of international awareness of what was actually happening in Terezín as well as a cameo featuring Egon Redlich whose fate was selected to illustrate one of the tens of thousands of human lives destroyed by the Nazis. At the end of this hall, visitors may be interested to read the recollections of the former inmates, arranged in thematic blocks.

Visitors may also like to watch more personal recollections of the Terezín Ghetto inmates on video-screens in this and the next hall. Called "Other Fates of Deportees", this hall introduces primarily the destinations to which the Terezín prisoners were deported, places of mass murders as well as those through which the Terezín inmates passed as slave laborers. For visitors' better orientation there are two large maps hanging on the walls.

At its end, the exhibition presents surveys displayed in the adjoining corridor and featuring various charts and lists of transports to and from Terezín, overviews of the total prison population classified according to their country of origin as well as data on the overall number of deportees, total number of deaths, the number of prisoners who came to Terezín in evacuation transports at the end of World War II, the number of people who died during a spotted fever epidemic at the end of the war, the number of prisoners sent to other places, and the number of survivors among the deportees.

(2) **View of the first exhibition room on the first (ground) floor of the Museum's building**

FIRST (GROUND) FLOOR OF THE BUILDING

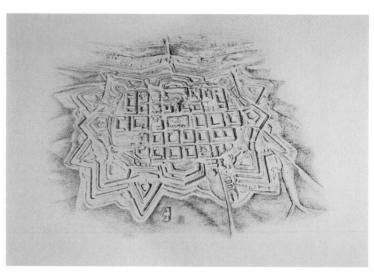

(3) **Fortress Terezín on a wall drawing by Milan Ressel on display in the first exhibition hall**

TEREZÍN'S FOUNDATION AND HISTORY

Terezín lies at the confluence of the Labe (Elbe) and Ohře (Eger) rivers, some 60 kilometers north-west of Prague. Terezín gained its international name due to the most tragic period in its history in World War II. Indeed, it came to symbolize the extermination of the Jewish population and the brutal persecution of Nazi Germany's political opponents in that period. But Terezín's checkered history dates back to the turn of the 18th century, when a decision was made to build a fortress to protect the road leading from Dresden through Lovosice to Prague as well as the major river route – the Labe. Its construction was further stimulated by the Habsburg monarchy's experience gained from its 18th century wars with Prussia. The military operations in the years 1741, 1744 and 1756 accentuated the true strategic importance of the territory between Lovosice – Litoměřice – Budyně nad Ohří. As a result, the first plan to build fortifications on the confluence of the Labe and Ohře rivers appeared already in 1757. The final decision to build a fortress was accelerated by another occupation of the Litoměřice district by the Prussian troops in 1778.

The foundation stone to the fortress was laid by Emperor Joseph II on October 10, 1780. By that time, construction work had already been under way for several months, and the Engineering Directorate, in charge of the whole project, was inaugurated on April 12, 1780. It was headed by Colonel Karl Niklas von Steinmetz, later promoted to the rank of General and appointed the first commander of the fortress. An imperial decree, issued on December 12, 1780, gave the newly built fortress the name Theresienstadt – in honor of Empress Maria Theresa. Construction work proceeded very fast, and already on September 22, 1784, Terezín was declared a closed town, its gates protected by guards. Terezín's inundation system was tested in the presence of its main designer General Karl Pellegrini in June 1790, and the fortress was proclaimed combat serviceable. All in all, as many as 1,500 bricklayers and masons and some 15,000 troops were involved in its construction. The financial costs of the project reached what was for that time a truly staggering sum of about 12,500,000 gold pieces.

The Terezín Fortress ranked among the absolute top in fortification engineering of its time. Its backbone consisted of 37 fortification elements in the Main Fortress, another 12 in the Small Fortress plus 6 elements in the fortified area between the Old and New Ohře. During the 19th century the overall perimeter of the fortress was expanded with the construction of new fortified works on the right bank of the Labe.

Consisting of an outer, central and inner defense zone, the fortress had at its disposal an extensive network of minefields in its underground galleries lined with a large complex of interconnecting corridors. The overall length of the mine tunnels, interconnecting corridors and eavesdropping galleries reached almost 30 kilometers. The Terezín mine system covered one third of the total perimeter of the fortress, the remaining two thirds were to be protected by the so-called inundation basins that could be flooded in case of danger. These covered an area of 158 hectares. Water also inundated the fortress moats.

The imperial decree on the settlement of Terezín issued on December 9, 1782, permitted the construction of civilian houses within the fortress, and Terezín was declared a royal town. The land inside its walls not used for military purposes was parceled out to offer as many as 288 building sites. Aimed at stimulating the settlement of Terezín, another decree was issued in the following year, exempting new settlers from the duty to pay taxes for 15 to 30 years. This depended on whether the construction of their houses was to be financed from settlers' own resources or from public loans. The prevailing architectural style of Terezín's civilian houses was determined by the local military authorities. No wonder then that their austere and practical designs had to be subordinated to the town's military character.

The Imperial Chancellery granted Terezín its coat-of-arms in 1846. By that time, Terezín was a distinctly German town. German was also the language of instruction in its elementary school, first mentioned in 1790. In the year 1836 the school was attended by 211 pupils. Terezín's economic and social life duly reflected its military garrison whose pride was primarily the Infantry Regiment No. 42, based in the town since 1817. One year earlier, the Duke of Wellington, the victor over Napoleon at Waterloo, became the honorary owner of the regiment.

After the outbreak of the Prussian-Austrian war in June 1866 large-scale preparations for the defense of the fortress got under way. But its garrison was not actually deployed in the fighting, restricting itself solely to guarding the Dresden – Prague railway line. Indeed, the course of that war cast serious doubts on the justification and military rationale of the very existence of the Terezín Fortress, which lost its strategic significance after Austro-Hungary and Germany concluded an alliance in 1879. Consequently, Terezín, whose fortress status had been abolished in 1888, became a garrison town where some three thousand troops were quartered. Two of its fortress gates – the Bohušovice and Litoměřice ones – were even pulled down in 1898, and part of the walls on the town's western edge followed suit. Public facilities were built, while new businesses and industrial plants were also set up to a limited extent. As years went by, the town's ethnic mix gradually changed and in the early 20th century the share of its Czech inhabitants heavily outnumbered its German population.

Originally called Fort B, the Small Fortress was built as an irregular rectangle whose western side adjoins the Old Ohře. Its main purpose was to protect the sluice gates of the inundation system on the Old Ohře, while guarding the Labe waterway within the shooting range of its artillery guns. Since its establishment the Small Fortress also served as "Festungs-Stockhaus" – an army penitentiary with a capacity of up to 800 inmates. Political prisoners were also incarcerated in the prison from the early 19th century. The best known among them was Alexandros K. Ypsilantis Jr., leader of the Greeks' anti-Turkish uprising from 1821, Polish Countess Anna Rożycka, Hungarian revolutionary Sándor Rozsa and Lojo Salih Vilajetovič, leader of the Bosnian national liberation movement.

During World War I the number of political prisoners jailed in the Small Fortress exceeded two and a half thousand. The best known prisoners were the ringleaders of the Sarayevo assassination. Both Gavrilo Princip, who fired the fatal shots in Sarayevo, which eventually proved to be a prologue to World War I, and his closest colleagues Trifko Grabež and Nedeljko Čabrinovič did not survive their imprisonment in the Small Fortress. Also incarcerated there were the rebels from the Seventh Rifle Regiment in Rumburk. As many as 300 of them languished in the cells of the Small Fortress until October 1918. Between 1914 and 1915 the Small Fortress also served as a prison for more than a thousand so-called Russophiles – Ruthenian inhabitants of Galicia, suspected of sympathies for Russia, the enemy of Austro-Hungary.

Thousands of Russian, Italian, Serbian and Romanian POWs were also jailed in Terezín, living in wooden barrack camps, built beyond the town in the direction of Počáply and České Kopisty and behind the Small Fortress near Trávčice. These prisoners either worked in the neighborhood or were sent for work, for instance, to the Ostrava mines and in agriculture. More than a thousand Russian POWs and hundreds of prisoners of other nationalities died of epidemics and malnutrition.

On October 28, 1918, the Czech population of Terezín gave an enthusiastic welcome to the proclamation of an independent Czechoslovak state. Following the departure of most of its German-speaking inhabitants, largely to the nearby town of Litoměřice, Terezín became an almost purely Czech town. In the years between the two world wars it witnessed truly turbulent developments in its political, public and cultural life. Unfortunately, its walls and military installations kept hampering a more substantial economic upsurge, and Terezín's military garrison still remained a decisive factor affecting its life.

Following the Munich conference in early October 1938, Terezín became, virtually overnight, a border town into which refugees from the border regions, seceded by Czechoslovakia and occupied by Hitler's Germany, streamed in their thousands. Hundreds of them found makeshift accommodation in Terezín for a shorter or longer period.

But the worst was yet to come. On March 15, 1939, the rest of the Czech lands was occupied by Nazi Germany as well. Two days later, the first political prisoners arrested during the "Aktion Gitter" (Action Bars) were put into the Small Fortress. This was just a temporary measure, as the Prague Gestapo Police Prison was set up in the Small Fortress in June 1940. Its inmates were mostly members of the Czech resistance organizations but also other groups of people, arrested during various waves of Nazi mass persecution, such as the relatives and people suspected of helping the Czech paratroopers involved in the assassination of the Acting Reich Protector Reinhard Heydrich in May 1942. Many prisoners were detained for acts of individual resistance. Some 90 percent of the inmates were Czech, the rest citizens of the then Soviet Union as well as

Poles, Yugoslavs, Frenchmen and members of other nationalities. But the worst fate and conditions in the prison were in store for Jewish prisoners coming from the nearby Ghetto to be punished or Jewish members of the Czech anti-Nazi resistance movement and persons defying the anti-Jewish regulations. By the end of the war, more than 32,000 people passed through the Small Fortress Prison, of whom a full 2,600 perished there. Some 300 inmates were executed, others were tortured to death by prison wardens or succumbed to epidemics, starvation and exhaustion. Out of all the inmates who had been sent from Terezín to other Nazi prisons, penitentiaries and concentration camps, 5,500 also died.

The Ghetto – reception and transit camp for Jewish prisoners – was established in the town of Terezín itself on November 24, 1941. It was originally intended for the concentration of Jewish inhabitants of the then Protectorate of Bohemia and Moravia. Jews from the Reich (Germany, Austria) began to arrive in mid-1942, later followed by deportees from the Netherlands, Denmark, Slovakia and Hungary. All in all, 140,000 Jews were deported to the Ghetto. At the end of the war, more than 15,000 prisoners evacuated before the approaching Allied armies from various concentration camps arrived in Terezín. Overall, 155,000 men, women and children passed through the Terezín Ghetto, more than 118,000 of them perished.

(4) **An object made up of the original transport suitcases in the first hall of the exhibition on the first (ground) floor of the Ghetto Museum**

)32·WEINEROVÁ HANA 22.11.1931·WEINGARTEN MILAN 10.4.1941·WEINHEBER TOMÁŠ 13.7.1928·WEINHEBER
0.1.1938·WEINSTEINOVÁ ZDEŇKA 30.4.1932·WEINSTEINOVÁ SOŇA 15.12.1932·WEINSTEINOVÁ JANA 2.6.1929·W
6.3.1934·WEISLOVÁ SOŇA 23.3.1930·WEISLOVÁ JANA 21.11.1941·WEISLOVÁ RUTH 7.9.1930·WEISNER RUTH 28.2.1
WEISS TOMÁŠ 5.11.1934·WEISS TOMÁŠ 10.9.1942·WEISS GEORG 12.8.1935·WEISS HANUŠ 12.1.1930·WEISS MILAN
17.7.1933·WEISSBARTHOVÁ VĚRA 17.11.1929·WEISSBARTL JAN 11.12.1932·WEISSBARTLOVÁ ALŽBĚTA 28.12.1930·W
5.11.1927·WEISSENSTEINOVÁ OLGA 16.3.1928·WEISSHUTOVÁ HANA 22.4.1937·WEISSKOPF PETR 15.11.1936·WEISS
·WEISSOVÁ JEANINA 13.8.1932·WEISSOVÁ SYLVIA 22.12.1933·WEISSOVÁ LIANA 7.12.1928·WEISSOVÁ VĚRA ERNE
VÁ LEA 24.8.1934·WEISSOVÁ HANNA 4.1.1939·WEISSOVÁ RUTH 22.6.1930·WEISSOVÁ THEODORA 13.1.1930·WEIS
ŠERGER IRÉN 14.9.1940·WEISZBERGER IREN 14.9.1940·WEISZOVÁ RUTH 19.12.1929·WEISZOVÁ EDITA 8.9.1932·W
30·WEJMAN MEJER 1929·WELDLER KURT 14.3.1936·WELDLER PAVEL 22.5.1937·WELKEROVÁ IRENA 9.11.1929·WE
35·WENGIER MONIEK 1934·WENGIER MONIA 1933·WENGRAFOVÁ DAGMAR 23.3.1931·WENGRAFOVÁ DORIT
·WERNER EDA 29.8.1928·WERNER FRANK 21.10.1943·WERNER PETER 12.10.1941·WERNER SUZANNE MARGOT 2
LILY 2.6.1932·WERTHEIMSTEIN JINDŘICH 28.11.1934·WERTHEIMSTEINOVÁ EVA 18.6.1933·WESSEL JOSEPHINE
R PETR 9.1.1931·WIENER GERTRUD 9.9.1942·WIENEROVÁ VĚRA 30.10.1930·WIENEROVÁ ALŽBĚTA 18.6.1939·WIE
.1932·WIJK VAN DER GRIETJE 5.1.1938·WIJK VAN DER JOZEF 12.8.1933·WIJNBERG CLARA ALIDA 5.12.1934·WILC
LLEY 8.3.1938·WILNIEWSKI ABRAM 1933·WILSCHIK BELA 8.3.1943·WILTSCHEKOVÁ RUTH 19.12.1934·WILZIG M
WINIK RUWA 1935·WINIK SZEJNA 1934·WINIK SRUL 1933·WINIK MOJSZE 1932·WINIK SZLOMA 1935·WINIK I
7·WINTERBERG ANNELIESE 6.1.1929·WINTERBERGER VALTR 1.8.1931·WINTERBERGER (KLEINBERGER) SALO 2
Á 20.5.1930·WINTERNITZOVÁ EVA 31.1.1935·WINTERNITZOVÁ HANA 22.3.1928·WINTERNITZOVÁ GERTA 30.5.19
·WINTEROVÁ VERONIKA LUCY 12.2.1936·WINTERSTEIN JINDŘICH 22.12.1931·WINTERSTEIN JIŘÍ 24.3.1932·WI
DRE 1.5.1929·WITTKOWSKY GERDA 29.5.1933·WITTKOWSKY HEINZ 18.6.1930·WITTLER PETR 25.8.1935·WITTLEF
. 28.11.1932·WOHL PAVEL 8.2.1931·WOHLGEMUTH GERD 22.2.1936·WOHLOVÁ DORITA 20.4.1928·WOKOWICKI
WOLF THEO 3.12.1930·WOLF HANUŠ PETR 22.4.1932·WOLF ALFRED 16.2.1932·WOLF FANNY 7.4.1929·WOLF OTT
5·WOLFF EWALD 21.4.1931·WOLFF GISELA BRANDA 28.7.1943·WOLFF HEINZ D. 16.9.1930·WOLFF LOUIS 26.3.192
EMA 12.10.1932·WOLFOVÁ JUDITA 5.4.1938·WOLFOVÁ JIŘINA 15.10.1931·WOLFOVITSCHOVÁ FRIMETTA 21.2.194
MARCELA 12.7.1937·WOLLNEROVÁ RUTH 29.11.1941·WOLLSTEINOVÁ EVA JULIE 24.1.1931·WORCH EVA 6.5.1929·1
UBEL ETKI 1933·WULWEKOVÁ KATEŘINA 2.6.1943·WULWEKOVÁ SYLVA 26.3.1935·WUNGROD CHAIM 1936·WUF
5.7.1943·WURZELOVÁ RUTH 30.8.1929·WURZINGER HANS 22.5.1933·WYGOLSKO ICCHOK 1937·WYLOZNY MEI
EL 1933·ZAGIEL NOSKE 1932·ZAGIEL MALKA 1931·ZACHARIA-GROKOP EWA 1933·ZACHARIA-GROKOP SARA 1
9·ZALUŽANSKÁ MILENA 28.7.1934·ZAPNER JIŘÍ 12.9.1928·ZAPNEROVÁ HANNA 21.7.1935·ZAPPNER TOMÁŠ 17.9.
AUEROVÁ DORA 15.12.1932·ZDROJANSKA DINA 1933·ZDROJANSKI NEACH 1936·ZECKENDORF TOMÁŠ 3.3.193
ZELMAN LEJB 1934·ZELMAN LEJZER 1934·ZEMANKOVÁ EVA 11.3.1939·ZENKER OTA 24.7.1929·ZENKER JIŘÍ 18.2.1
VA 1.2.1942·ZENTNEROVÁ RŮŽENA 26.3.1933·ZENTNEROVÁ SONJA 8.4.1935·ZIEGELMANN HERMANN 30.9.1937
ZIMMER PAVEL 17.7.1928·ZIMMERMANNOVÁ ERNA 14.7.1933·ZIMMERMANNOVÁ EVA 15.2.1935·ZIMMEROVÁ I
ZUCKER JIŘÍ 2.8.1938·ZUCKERMANN LEO 25.2.1936·ZUCKERMANNOVÁ ZUZANA 28.12.1933·ZULTY BELKA 1930
12.9.1934·ZUNTERSTEINOVÁ OLGA 13.11.1929·ZUNTERSTEINOVÁ VILMA 15.12.1932·ZUNTZ HARRY 14.5.1933·ZU
AL JIŘÍ 15.11.1934·ZWEIGENTHAL VIKTOR 9.9.1930·ZWEIGENTHAL PAVEL 18.6.1928·ZWEIGENTHAL OTTO 6.4.1
AWRFM 1934·ZYLBERBLAT CHASIA 1934·ZYLBERSTEIN JANKIEL 1937·ZYSKIND GUTA 1936·ZYSKIND RACHEL

(5) The walls of the Memorial Hall commemorating the youngest victims of the Terezín Ghetto are covered with the names of 8,000 children

THE YOUNGEST VICTIMS

The Terezín Ghetto's prison population included more than 10,500 children who had not yet reached the age of 15 before their deportation. About 400 of them died in Terezín. A critical moment in the lives of most of the inmates came with their deportation order to transports to the extermination camps in the East, where some 7,500 of the youngest victims of the "Final Solution of the Jewish Question" perished. According to contemporary surveys, no more than 245 children from Terezín returned from the transports to the East.

The building now housing the Ghetto Museum was closely associated with the fate of the youngest inmates. Formerly a municipal school, this object – designated in the Ghetto as L 417 – housed children's homes for boys aged 10 to 15. It was the object L 417, or rather its young inhabitants, that excelled among the remaining children's homes in other buildings in the town, mostly thanks to the overall level of their cultural and social activities. The boys in that home attended secret school classes, debates and cultural programs given by leading scientists, artists and politicians also deported to the Ghetto. These young people were systematically encouraged in their love for knowledge and cultural pursuits. Thanks to their outstanding teachers and educators but also to their own activities the boys living in L 417 managed to turn it into a true hub of youth activities in the Ghetto.

Part of the exhibition in the Ghetto Museum also shows – in addition to several photos of children taken during a visit to Terezín paid by a delegation of the International Committee of the Red Cross on June 23, 1944 – photographs of several dozens of the Terezín children before their deportation to the Ghetto. The latter pictures show happy boys and girls looking ahead not only to their youth but to their whole lives. And yet, only a handful of the captive children and virtually none of their teachers and educators escaped their tragic fate.

A well-selected set of the famous drawings by the children from the Terezín Ghetto shows that these young artists depicted in their drawings what they had actually seen in the Ghetto only marginally. Much more often they returned in their mind's eye to their home, to the days of their freedom, conjuring up a realm of fairy tales and dreams, and expressing their aspirations for freedom and life amidst exquisite nature.

Fears of the future were much more succinctly reflected in their literary works, primarily in what were their often surprisingly mature poems. These include the poem called *Zahrada* (Garden) by the 14-year old František Bass. He wrote about a boy who would no longer live when a flower bud blossoms out in his garden. Thanks to its simple and moving narrative and its tragic undertones this poem marks the motto of the whole first (ground) floor of the Ghetto Museum. Its second hall is conceived as a Memory Hall commemorating the youngest victims of the Terezín Ghetto. Covering its walls are some 8,000 names of those helpless creatures whose lives were nipped in the bud, to use a literary phrase. This is not a complete list since to this day nobody has managed to find the names of all the children killed by the Nazis. However, research into the fate of the children from the Terezín Ghetto continues unabated, and each new name to be discovered will be added to the walls of the Memorial Hall.

In actual fact, each name on the wall represents a particular boy or girl who once cherished their own dreams, hopes and childhood loves. All that was murdered together with them. And that is why the underlying message of their destroyed lives, which has been coming through to us since the end of World War II, should never be forgotten.

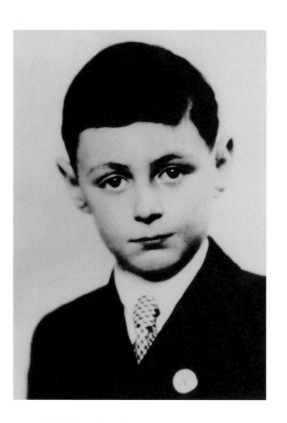

(6) Lea Pollak (March 21, 1930 – May 18, 1944, Auschwitz) and her brother Josef (January 27, 1933 – May 18, 1944, Auschwitz)

Photographs showing several of the Terezín Ghetto's youngest victims before their deportation

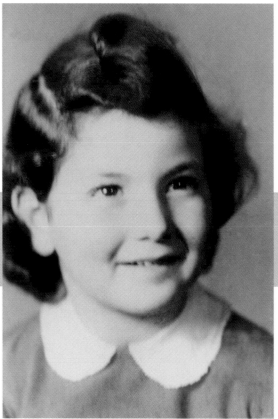

(7) Zdeněk Koňas (June 23, 1932 – September 6, 1943, Auschwitz)

(8) Marie Castelinová (February 4, 1938 – October 4, 1944, Auschwitz)

(9, 10) **Photographs of the children in the Terezín Ghetto taken during a visit paid by a delegation of the International Committee of the Red Cross. Several months later these children were gassed in Auschwitz**

A little garden,
Fragrant and full of roses.
The path is narrow
And a little boy walks along it.

A little boy, a sweet boy,
Like that growing blossom.
When the blossom comes to bloom,
The little boy will be no more.

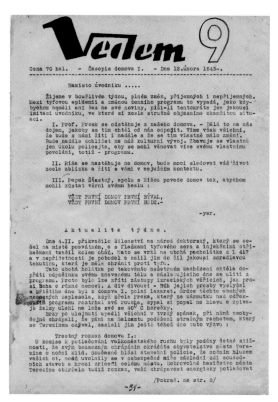

(11) Using simple words, František Bass's poem *Zahrada* (Garden) spells out the tragic fate of the author and his contemporaries in the Ghetto. The 14-year old author of the poem perished in Auschwitz on October 28, 1944

(12) "Vedem" was the most important of the magazines produced in the children's homes housed in object L 417

Only drawings have often been left behind by many children from the Terezín Ghetto. Before their young lives had been destroyed the young artists captured in their drawings all their emotions, aspirations and thoughts. Thanks to their simple beauty the drawings made by the children from the Terezín Ghetto point an accusing finger at the heinous crime whose victims the young artists became

(13) Hanuš Fischl (September 26, 1933 – October 6, 1944, Auschwitz)

(14) Liliana Franklová (January 12, 1931 – October 19, 1944, Auschwitz)

(15) Julie Agularová (June 13, 1933 – October 6, 1944, Auschwitz)

(16) Ruth Heinová (February 19, 1934 – October 23, 1944, Auschwitz)

19

(17) A collage of drawings by the children from the Terezín Ghetto, on display on the staircase, connects the exhibition premises on the first (ground) floor, commemorating primarily the youngest victims of the Ghetto, with the historical-documentary section of the exhibition on the second floor

True centerpiece of the collage is formed by the documentary drawings by Helga Weissová-Hošková (November 10, 1929, survived), showing scenes from everyday life in the Terezín Ghetto through children's eyes

(18) Helga Weissová: Children going to school, 1942

(19) Helga Weissová: Arrival in Terezín, 1942

(20) A poster stand covered with anti-Jewish notices
and regulations from the time of the Nazi occupation
is situated at the entrance to the historical-
documentary section of the exhibition on the second
floor

PLOTTING GENOCIDE

PLOTTING GENOCIDE

The main ideological and political pillars of Hitler's National Socialist German Workers' Party (NSDAP) were based on hatred of the Jews, fabrications of a worldwide Jewish plot, and claims that the Jews were the primal cause of all evil in history. The first anti-Jewish discriminatory and persecutory measures were announced soon after the Nazis came to power in Germany on January 30, 1933. The Nazi Party's anti-Semitic propaganda was designed to pave the way for other persecution steps to follow. These were aimed at registering all the future victims of the Nazi genocide, isolating them from the rest of the population, excluding them from public and political life, and robbing them of their property and economic base. As of September 15, 1935, the Nazi persecution of the Jews proceeded according to would-be legislative norms declared during a Nazi Party Convention in Nuremberg, which came to be known as the Nuremberg Laws. Pursuant to them, the Jews formally lost their civic and human rights. They were deprived of their Reich citizenship and designated merely "subjects of the state". Their marriages to and extramarital relations with "Aryans" were banned, and a definition of Jewishness, used to determine who is to be classified as Jew or "first- and second-level 'mischlinge' (part-Jews)", was also enacted. In later years, these regulations, first applied in Germany, were introduced also in the Nazi-dominated countries.

As years went by, the measures aimed at persecuting the Jews were further promoted and specified, acquiring the form of brutal terror. Following assassination of a German diplomat by a Jewish boy in Paris, the Nazis carried out a pogrom code-named "Kristallnacht" (Night of Broken Glass) throughout Hitler's Reich on the night of November 9, 1938. Jews were tortured and killed, their flats, stores and other property vandalized, synagogues were demolished and burnt. Some 30,000 Jews were herded into concentration camps, and what was more the Jewish population was ordered to pay contributions worth one billion marks, a sum later used for Germany's armaments program.

On January 30, 1939 Adolf Hitler told the Reichstag (German Parliament): "Today I will be a prophet again: If international finance Jewry within Europe and abroad should succeed once more in plunging the peoples into a world war, then the consequence will not be the Bolshevization of the world and therewith a victory of Jewry, but on the contrary, the destruction of the Jewish race in Europe!" With a good deal of cynicism he thus branded the Jews as the potential culprits of a war he was planning to unleash himself very soon. Unfortunately, many people still did not take his threat of the physical liquidation of the Jews very seriously.

The racial regulations proceeding from the Nuremberg Laws came into effect in the Czech lands first in the border areas seceded to Germany under the agreement between Germany, France, Italy and Great Britain, concluded in Munich on September 30, 1938. Less than six months later, on March 15, 1939, Hitler's Germany occupied the rest of the Czech lands. Called the Protectorate of Bohemia and Moravia, this territory was declared part of the Great German Reich. Following on from there, the anti-Jewish measures in the Protectorate were imposed either directly by the German occupation authorities or by the Protectorate government and its local authorities. These regulations ranged from the restriction of shopping times for the Jews to a ban on raising domestic animals in their households. Their ultimate purpose was to humiliate and sap the will of the Jewish population who was to be branded a sign of inferiority.

However, the German occupation authorities prevented those eager domestic quislings, recruited from the ranks of Czech fascists and Protectorate officials, from taking any part in the plundering of Jewish property. That was why the process known as "Aryanization", i.e. organized robbery of Jewish property, was concentrated solely in the Nazi hands. Their strategy stemmed from the assumption that the solution of the "Jewish Question" would be followed by an eventual solution of the Czech Question. As a result, "Aryanization" became one of the tools in the gradual implementation of the Germanization of the Czech territory. A point of departure for its realization was the directive on Jewish property issued on June 21, 1939, by Reich Protector Konstantin von Neurath. This officially introduced the Nuremberg Laws in the Protectorate, a legislation including the provision that subjected to "Aryanization" were not only enterprises with a Jewish property share but also those "under Jewish influence". This involved not only large and medium-size property, all the Jews were robbed of their possessions.

During the first period of Nazi occupation the German authorities supported Jewish emigration. In order to ensure coordinated proceedings of all the relevant authorities, a Central Office for Jewish Emigration was established in Prague in July 1939, modeled on a similar institution in Vienna and renamed in 1942 the Central Office for the Settlement of the Jewish Question in Bohemia and Moravia. It was initially headed by Adolf Eichmann, later the notorious chief of the Jewish department in the Reich Security Main Office (RSHA) in Berlin. His successor, who held the post till the end of the country's Nazi occupation, was Hans Günther.

Even though emigration represented a painful decision for each Jewish family, resulting in the loss of their existing social and economic status, in severing their familial links as well as in the loss of their property, it eventually proved to be a lucky step for those who managed to leave the country. After some 19,000 people emigrated in 1939, the rate of Jewish emigration quickly dropped, virtually grinding to a halt in 1942. All in all, 26,000 Jews were allowed to leave the Czech lands legally. However, many fled from the Protectorate illegally, joining the Czechoslovak military units abroad. There were many other Jews who took an active part in the anti-fascist resistance movement in the Protectorate or went into hiding, helped by their "Aryan" fellow citizens.

As many as 136 Jewish religious communities, 379 Jewish associations providing mostly assistance and cultural programs, and some 6,780 foundations pursuing charitable and educational purposes existed in the Czech lands in 1939. After the German occupation, the work evolved by such associations and foundations was quickly terminated, and the overall number of Jewish religious communities was drastically reduced. In July 1939 there were only 14 such communities outside the capital, while the Jewish Religious Community in Prague had been given official responsibility for proper functioning of those communities. The Prague Community, itself subordinated to the Central Office for Jewish Emigration,

was gradually charged with administrative tasks ranging from various reporting duties and tax collection to emigration and deportation agenda. It was also responsible for the registration of all the Jews. Its officials tried their best to alleviate the harsh social impact of the anti-Jewish regulations but the Jewish Religious Community's possibilities proved to be very limited indeed. To a large extent, the Prague Jewish Religious Community organized retraining courses for people who had been banned from performing their original professions. A retraining camp established at Lípa near Německý (today Havlíčkův) Brod was attended by 1,353 Jewish men.

Some of the officials of the Prague Jewish Religious Community were persecuted for their resistance activities and sabotage. For instance, Hanuš Bonn, Head of the Emigration Department, was sent to the Mauthausen concentration camp and executed there for sabotaging the first deportations of Czech Jews.

Still, the persecution of the young generation of the Jewish population had the most painful and distressing effect of all. As the Jews were expected by the Nazis to have no future at all, education of Jewish children was systematically curtailed. As of the beginning of the school year 1940/1941, Jewish pupils and students were expelled from all the Czech schools, while the possibility of their education at Jewish schools and home teaching groups turned out to be only a temporary arrangement. A total ban on any form of education of Jewish children was to follow shortly.

Already after the German attack on and defeat of Poland in the fall of 1939 the plans for the deportation of Jewish inhabitants began to receive specific contours. As part of the plan to concentrate Jews in the south-eastern part of the General Gouvernement (the Nazi-occupied Polish territory not directly incorporated into the Reich), two transports of Jewish male prisoners left Ostrava for Nisko upon San on October 18 and 27, 1939. However, this operation was suspended due to different reasons, the remaining deportees returning to Ostrava in April (1940).

Mass deportations of the Jews from the Protectorate started in the fall of 1941. Several checks were made in preparation for those deportations of all the persons meeting the definition of Jewishness under the Nuremberg Laws. The lists compiled during the last registration in October 1941 contained the names of 88,105 people, the future victims of the "Final Solution of the Jewish Question".

Der Stürmer

...sches Wochenblatt zum Kampfe um die Wahrheit

HERAUSGEBER : JULIUS STREICHER

Sonder-Nummer

Preis 20 Pfennig

Sonder-nummer 11 — Erscheint wöchentl. Einzel-Nr. 20 Pfg. Bezugspreis monatlich 54 Pfg. zuzüglich Postbestellgeld. Bestellungen bei dem Briefträger oder der zuständ. Postanstalt. Nachbestellungen a. b. Verlag. Schluß der Anzeigenannahme 14 Tage vor Erscheinen. Preis für Gerichts-Anz. Die ca. 22 mm breite, 1 mm hohe Raum-Zeile im Anzeigenteil —.75 RM.

Nürnberg, im November 1938

Verlag: Der Stürmer, Julius Streicher, Nürnberg-N., Pfannenschmiedsgasse 19. Verlagsleitung: Max Fink, Nürnberg-N., Pfannenschmiedsgasse 19. Fernsprecher 21550. Postscheckkonto Amt Nürnberg Nr. 105. Schriftleitung Nürnberg-N., Pfannenschmiedsgasse 19. Fernsprecher 21572. Schriftleitungsschluß Freitag (nachmittags). Briefanschrift: Nürnberg 2, Schließfach 305.

16. Jahr 1938

Der Jude
und die
Tschecho=Slowakei

Der Zusammenbruch

In diesen Tagen brach im Osten Europas ein sogenannter „Staat" in seiner bisherigen Form zusammen. Die Tschechoslowakei. Sie brach in ihre Bestandteile auseinander. Die deutschen Volksgenossen und die deutschen Landstriche kehrten nach Deutschland zurück. Die Polen kehrten zurück nach Polen, die Magyaren nach Ungarn. Heute bildet die ehemalige Tschechoslowakei einen Bundesstaat, bestehend aus der Tschechei, aus der Slowakei und aus der Karpatho-Ukraine. Warum ist diese Entwicklung gekommen?

Die ehemalige Tschechoslowakei war zum Kriegsschluß durch den Vertrag von St. Germain entstanden und konstruiert worden. Es waren in diesen „Staat" gezwungen worden:

　　4 Millionen Deutsche,
　　2½ Millionen Slowaken,
　　700 000 Ungarn,
　　600 000 Ukrainer,
　　100 000 Polen.

Besonders gegen die Deutschen war in der Tschechoslowakei ein erbarmungsloser und grausamer Vernichtungskrieg geführt worden. Sie sollten durch systematische Zerschlagung ihrer wirtschaftlichen Existenz beseitigt und ausgerottet werden. Daneben wurden sie in ihrer Freiheit unterdrückt und auf das ungeheuerlichste gequält und gepeinigt. Verfolgungswelle auf Verfolgungswelle gingen seit 20 Jahren über das leidgeprüfte sudetendeutsche Land hinweg. Dies steigerte sich besonders in den letzten Wochen und Monaten bis zur Unerträglichkeit.

Zu diesem planmäßigen Vernichtungskrieg, der gegen die Sudetendeutschen geführt wurde, kam noch das beleidigende und herausfordernde Verhalten der Tschechoslowakei Deutschland gegenüber. Besonders seit dem Jahre 1933, dem Jahre der nationalsozialistischen Revolution, führte die Presse in diesem Lande einen ständigen, haßerfüllten Verleumdungs- und Hetzfeldzug gegen das Deutsche Reich.

Das geschächtete Slawentum

Dieses Bild stammt von dem tschechischen Maler Rélink. Es ist einer der wenigen Antisemiten in der Tschechei. Seine Schriften und Werke ließ Benesch verbieten. Rélink zeigt der Öffentlichkeit mit diesem Bild den Mörder der slawischen Völker: Es ist der Jude!

Die Juden sind unser Unglück!

(21) **The magazine "Der Stürmer" became a symbol of anti-Jewish Nazi propaganda**

(22) Hatred of the Jews was to be instilled in children already at school – one of the textbooks entitled "Der Giftpilz" (Poisonous Mushroom)

(24) Organized violence against the Jews reached its climax during the "Kristallnacht" (Night of Broken Glass) pogrom. Burning synagogue in Baden-Baden

(23) The Nuremberg Laws laid down the principles for identifying Jews and "first- and second-level 'mischlinge' (part-Jews)"

(25) The German occupation forces entering Prague on March 15, 1939. Standing between the police officers is a Jewish boy, Zdeněk Kárný who eventually died in an Auschwitz gas chamber on midnight of September 29, 1944

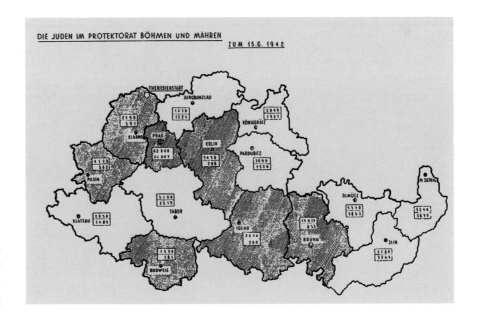

(26) Map of the Protectorate marking its Oberlandrats (districts). The upper figures in boxes give the number of the Jews living in the individual Oberlandrats in 1939, the figures below refer to the situation on June 15, 1942

(27) Hanuš Bonn, Head of the Emigration Department of the Jewish Religious Community in Prague, was arrested for sabotaging preparations for the first deportation transports and executed in Mauthausen in October 1941

(28) Photo showing the registration of the Jews

(29) After their expulsion from Czech schools, Jewish pupils were allowed, for a time, to attend Jewish schools (one is pictured here). A total ban on the education of Jewish children was issued in 1942

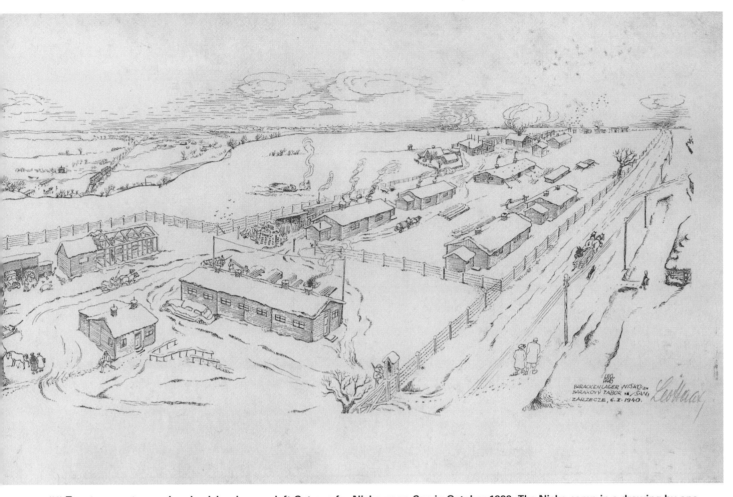

BARACKENLAGER NISKO am
BARAKOVÝ TABOR n./SANI
ZARZECZE, 6.X.1940.

(30) **Two transports carrying Jewish prisoners left Ostrava for Nisko upon San in October 1939. The Nisko camp in a drawing by one its inmates, Leo Haas**

(31) **View of the first exhibition room on the second floor**

(32) **View of the main exhibition room on the second floor**

GHETTO, LATER THE "JEWISH SETTLEMENT TERRITORY" – RECEPTION AND TRANSIT CAMP FOR JEWISH PRISONERS IN TEREZÍN

The "Final Solution of the Jewish Question", as the Nazis euphemistically called their plan to exterminate European Jewry, entered a new phase in the second half of 1941. The killing of the Jews was then unleashed on a truly mass scale, first in the occupied territories of the then Soviet Union. That task was entrusted to the SS units and the police forces subordinated to them. The coordinator of all these operations was Reinhard Heydrich, the Chief of the Reich Security Main Office, who received an official order from Hermann Göring, the Chairman of the Ministerial Council for the Defense of the Reich, on July 31, 1941.

By that time, Hitler was impatient and demanded that the Jews should be removed as soon as possible from the territory of what was then the Great German Reich, including the Protectorate of Bohemia and Moravia. The original plan anticipated that the Jews would be deported to the occupied Soviet territories only after the end of the military campaign in the East. However, under the impression of the great advances of the German armies in the first weeks and months of the war, Hitler issued an instruction in the middle of September 1941 to carry out that operation as soon as possible. Seen in the light of his earlier instruction to "cleanse" the occupied territories of the Jews, this amounted to an explicit order for the immediate murder of the deportees.

Heinrich Himmler, the Reichsführer of the SS, as well as Reinhard Heydrich seemed to be well aware of the formidable organizational and technical problems involved. In view of the demands by the army's high command for "communications capacities" and complaints of the "workload" of the death squads from the SS Einsatzgruppen (special task force groups), the Jews from the Reich and the Protectorate were first expected to be transported to the Ghetto in Łódź, and only later gradually deported to the places of extermination. But the plan ran up against the opposition of the local occupation authorities who referred to the overcrowding of the Łódź Ghetto. Seen in this light, a temporary solution had to be sought.

On September 27, 1941, Reinhard Heydrich also assumed the post of the Acting Reich Protector in Bohemia and Moravia, a move that eventually led to an escalation of anti-Jewish measures and accelerated preparations for the next stage of the "Final Solution" in the Protectorate. Heydrich devoted one of the very first conferences of his inner staff on October 10, 1941, to the subject of the "Final Solution". Proceeding from the conclusions of that conference, several thousand of the "most troublesome" Jews from the Protectorate were deported to the ghettos in Łódź and Minsk in October and November 1941, the rest of the Jews were to be concentrated somewhere in the territory of the Czech lands. Terezín was singled out as the most suitable site for this purpose. This decision was then definitely confirmed at another consultative meeting on October 17, 1941. All of a sudden, 50,000 to 60,000 Jewish prisoners were to be crammed into Terezín, a town where some 3,500 civilian inhabitants and approximately the same number of troops had lived before the war. In less than a year Terezín's prison population swelled to that level.

At the order of the Central Office for Jewish Emigration, the Jewish Religious Community in Prague also had to be involved in preparations for the establishment of the Terezín Ghetto. The German occupation forces did their utmost to create the impression among the members of the Jewish community that the Ghetto would be a self-governing territory where the Jews would be left to live and work until the end of the war. This was meant to help in maintaining peace among the future victims of the genocide, while giving the Nazis enough time for their planned and gradual liquidation of the Jews without disturbing the life in the Protectorate.

A group of 342 young Jewish men, members of the so-called construction gang, arrived in Terezín's Sudeten Barracks on November 24, 1941. Their job was to prepare the barracks in the town for the reception of the forthcoming transports, which started coming in to the emerging Ghetto on November 30, 1941. Transport was a term most aptly symbolizing the fate of the people who found themselves in the grips of the monstrous machinery known as the "Final Solution of the Jewish Question". To receive a deportation order to Terezín meant a total break with all the contacts and ties of one's previous life and a start of a sinister journey to the unknown. The Jews who had received their deportation orders gathered in designated collecting points in major Czech and Moravian towns. Before doing so they had to hand over all their property, keeping only a maximum of 50 kilos of luggage. Within a matter of several days the administrative formalities were sorted out at the collection points, after which the transports left for Terezín. Having arrived in the Ghetto, the Jews were herded into barracks where they lived under the most primitive conditions. Initially, families were allowed to stay together, but very soon they were divided, and men, women and children were mostly accommodated in separate barracks. This only served to step up mental pressure on the inmates. During the first month alone as many as 7,354 Jews from the Protectorate were deported to Terezín. Gradually, some 74,000 Jews were to pass through the gates of the Ghetto before the end of the war. Transports arrived at the railway station at Bohušovice nad Ohří, some 2.5 kilometers from Terezín, a distance all the Jews had to travel on foot. Many of the old and sick prisoners did not survive that journey.

The SS headquarters, headed by the Camp Commander, proved to be an absolute master over the life and death of the inmates. The post of the Camp Commander was held by Siegfried Seidl, Anton Burger and Karl Rahm respectively, all of them having the rank of SS-Obersturmführer (Seidl was promoted to the rank of SS-Hauptsturmführer during his stay in Terezín). The headquarters was subordinated to the Prague-based Central Office for Jewish Emigration, the brain-center of the "Final Solution of the Jewish Question" in the Protectorate. The members of the SS headquarters tormented the inmates mostly indirectly through a system of orders and bans aimed at making the life of each inmate as unpleasant and miserable as possible. But the SS officers also ill-treated the prisoners directly, especially in the infamous bunker beneath the SS Camp headquarters where "offenders" were interrogated and tortured. Two mass executions were staged in the Ghetto in January and February 1942. Inmates who had committed paltry misdemeanors, such as unauthorized dispatch of news from the Ghetto or a failure to greet an SS officer, were hanged. In an effort to maintain order in the camp and to forestall a pos-

sible uprising the SS Camp headquarters later took a different course. Offending prisoners were sent to the Prague Gestapo Police Prison in the Small Fortress where treatment of the Jewish inmates was so cruel as to match that practiced in a Nazi extermination camp. Another method of physical liquidation was deportation of inmates to the East with the so-called Weisung (special order), which – in practical terms – meant summary execution of the person concerned as soon as his or her transport arrived in the final destination.

Guard and escort duties in the Ghetto were performed by a special unit of the Protectorate gendarmerie. Generally speaking, the rank-and-file members of this unit treated the prisoners quite humanely, on occasions even expressing and showing their solidarity with them. In many cases, they helped the inmates to keep in touch with the outside world running formidable risks for themselves. In actual fact, the bulk of the guards differed from their commanding officers, the Nazi henchmen First Lieutenant Janeček (who soon assumed a Germanized version of his name – Janetschek) and his successor Lieutenant Hasenkopf. Both men tried to emulate the members of the SS Camp headquarters in their persecution and torture of the inmates. As many as 14 Czech gendarmes were imprisoned in the Small Fortress for giving assistance to the inmates, two of them did not survive their incarceration.

Just like the other ghettos and concentration camps, a Jewish Self-Administration was set up in the Terezín Ghetto as well. However, both the senior management of this self-governing body and its administration had to tow the Nazi line and discharge the SS orders, having only minimal opportunities and powers to ease the prisoners' hardships. An Elder of the Jews (Judenältester) with his deputy stood at the head of the Self-Administration, while the Council of Elders (Ältestenrat) served as a consultative body. The post of the Elder of the Jews in Terezín was held by Jakob Edelstein, Paul Eppstein and Benjamin Murmelstein respectively. The Self-Administration was divided into its Central Secretariat and five main departments. Later on their number rose to 9, including the Central Secretariat, and the Internal Affairs, Economic, Financial, Technical, Healthcare and Social Care Departments, Labor Center, Youth Care Department and Leisure Time Department.

Initially, the Self-Administration officials hoped that the Terezín Ghetto would be a labor camp whose production would be so significant as to protect its inmates from further deportations. However, these illusions were soon dashed. On January 5, 1942, the Ghetto's order of the day, which regularly published instructions and commands for the prisoners, announced a forthcoming transport to Riga, the first out of 63 transports to leave Terezín. During the first half of 1942 alone, 16,001 prisoners left in transports, followed, until the end of the year, by another 27,870 people. Their destinations were ghettos, concentration and extermination camps in the territory of Poland and the then Soviet Union. After the war, many of those names became quite notorious all over the world as synonyms for mass extermination – Treblinka, Majdanek, Maly Trostinec and others. As of October 26, 1942, all the transports from Terezín – with the exception of two small ones to Bergen-Belsen – had a single destination: the concentration and extermination camp Auschwitz II - Birkenau.

Each prisoner lived in constant fear of receiving a deportation order for an Eastern transport which grew to be a source of constant tension turning into horror during each announcement of a forthcoming transport. The fact that the SS Camp headquarters mostly fixed the quotas for each transport and the Self-Administration was obliged – to a large degree – to put in the necessary number of names was a major source of incessant conflicts, moral traumas as well as a breeding ground for corruption. But in the end, all the Terezín inmates sooner or later received their deportation orders for the transports, and only the end of the war could bring them liberation.

On January 20, 1942, the notorious Wannsee Conference, attended by the top-ranking SS commanders and state administration officials and chaired by Heydrich, discussed further proceedings in the implementation of the heinous program dubbed as the "Final Solution of the Jewish Question". A new mission was ascribed to Terezín by that conference. From then on, Terezín was to serve not only as a reception and transit camp for the Jews from the Protectorate but also as a ghetto for the elderly Jews (Altersghetto) from the Reich (Germany and Austria). The Ghetto was intended primarily for people over 65 years of age but also for holders of high awards, for war invalids as well as politicians, scientists and other people known to have close ties with foreign countries. The purpose of this particular measure was to ward off mounting foreign criticism, complaints and interventions on behalf of well-known Jews, and – by concentrating elderly people in Terezín – to add greater credence to the claims that Jewish transports to the East actually headed to

labor camps. Addressing a meeting of his staff in the Berlin Gestapo Central Office on March 6, 1942, Adolf Eichmann said that Terezín had been selected as an old people's ghetto to "save its face towards the outside world".

The new mission to be accomplished by the Terezín Ghetto also necessitated an extension of its accommodation capacity. Until then the prisoners were concentrated in 11 guarded barracks throughout the town. Earlier on, civilians also lived in Terezín, and the inmates were allowed to move around the town only under escort. After the Wannsee Conference, the whole town had to be turned into a large camp. Issued on February 16, 1942, Heydrich's decree abolished the municipality of Terezín, ordering its civilian population to move out by the end of June.

In keeping with the decision announced at the Wannsee Conference, transports of elderly people and "prominent personalities", initially only from Germany and Austria, as of 1943 also involving Jews from other countries under the German occupation, namely the Netherlands, Denmark, Slovakia, and Hungary, started arriving in Terezín still before its civilian population had left the town. The first transport from Berlin came already on June 2, 1942, to be followed, later that month, by another 13 transports from Berlin and 10 from Munich. The first transports from Vienna arrived on June 21 and 29. However, these were just forerunners of many other transports to follow. During the second half of 1942 alone, as many as 124 transports arrived from Germany, bringing in 30,989 prisoners, 11 transports came from Austria carrying 11,922 prisoners, while 8 transports brought 355 people from the occupied border regions of the Czech lands. In actual fact, the hardships of the life in the Ghetto meant a terrible shock especially for so many new arrivals, mostly older people. Before their departure, the German Jews were forced to conclude what were called contracts for the purchase of homes, for which they paid with all their possessions. But instead of lifelong accommodation in a spa town, promised by the Nazis, the German Jews were in for the harsh reality of the Terezín Ghetto.

Due to the influx of new transports, the Ghetto reached the limits of its peak accommodation capacity in September 1942. During that month there were 58,491 prisoners in Terezín as compared with 12,968 inmates in April of that year. No wonder that this was reflected in a dramatic rise in the mortality rate. While 259 people died in the Ghetto in April, the death-rate in August soared to 2,327 and to as many as 3,941 in September. An indescribable chaos would often prevail in the camp – everything was mixed up, people from the incoming transports were accommodated with great difficulty, being placed in attics, casemates in the old fortifications as well as in sheds in yards. The old people, especially from Germany and Austria, were heavily traumatized, and in their hopelessness they quickly succumbed to diseases and hunger. Between April and September (1942) Terezín's prison population quadrupled, the number of deaths soared more than 15-fold. The SS Camp headquarters had a very simple recipe to solve the problem of overcrowding in the Ghetto – to dispatch thousands of people to the places of extermination in the East. Nobody was saved out of the total of 16,004 people who had left Terezín in 8 transports of the elderly in the fall 1942. The first people to leave in those transports were old German Jews who had bought their new "homes" in Terezín. Tongue in cheek, Heinrich Himmler, the Reichsführer of the SS, declared during an audience with the Italian dictator Mussolini on October 11, 1942: "The remaining elderly Jews have been housed in the small town of Terezín, a Jewish retirement ghetto, where they receive their pensions and benefits and can do as they will with their life…"

Soon after this cynical statement by Himmler, the Nazis' self-confidence was shattered by the military failures of Hitler's Germany on World War II fronts. The defeat at Stalingrad, the Allies' successful landing in Northern Africa and other setbacks suffered by the Wehrmacht affected the further procedures in the implementation of the "Final Solution of the Jewish Question". This was reflected in the temporary suspension of the transports of Terezín prisoners to the East. An appropriate order was given by Himmler himself who added that "the impression should not be disturbed that Terezín is indeed a place where the Jews may live and die in peace". Shortly before that, on December 18, 1942, the governments of 12 Allied countries, including the Czechoslovak government in exile, issued a declaration condemning the extermination of European Jewry and emphasizing that the authors and perpetrators of those crimes would be held accountable after the war. There were growing requests from international organizations, primarily the International Committee of the Red Cross, to visit the final destinations of the transports carrying the deported Jews. Seen in this light, Terezín was to play an increased propaganda role, serving as a smoke-screen covering up the criminal nature of the "Final Solution".

The forced break in transports nurtured hopes among the inmates that the transports had, indeed, been stopped for good. But that was not what the SS headquarters had in mind. This was solely a temporary measure enforced by the novel situation that manifested itself in other events as well. Already in the fall of 1942 "stores" were established in Terezín where prisoners could buy with vouchers some kinds of goods, confiscated earlier from their luggage on arrival in the camp. In December of the same year the Ghetto even opened a "café" where those who obtained tickets could sit for an hour and a half sipping ersatz coffee and listening to popular music. But that was just the beginning. In the spring of 1943 Terezín underwent a "beautification" campaign to set the stage for what was actually a theater performance of its kind – a visit by a foreign delegation. In May 1943, the Bank of the Jewish Self-Administration was opened in Terezín, issuing its own – yet valueless – money. Some time later, the streets of Terezín were given names instead of their former numbers. Thus, for instance, the former L 1 was renamed Lake Street even though there was no lake far and wide. On June 28, 1943, Terezín was visited by a delegation, which – besides representatives of some offices included officials of the German Red Cross. Nevertheless, Adolf Eichmann, who accompanied the delegation, declared after the visit that thorough preparations would still have to be made before Terezín could be presented to a full-fledged foreign delegation.

In the spring of 1943 the prisoners built a road bypassing the town and primarily a railway siding. That went into service on June 1, 1943, enabling transport trains to come directly into the town and to leave it. As a result, the shocking picture of incoming and outgoing transports, an image which was deeply engraved in the memory of all the inmates, remained hidden at least to the eyes of the people living in the vicinity. During the temporary break in the transports sent to the East, Terezín's prison population kept rising, exceeding the 45,000 mark in August 1943. Furthermore, the camp's accommodation capacity was considerably limited after the Sudeten Barracks and several other larger objects had been speedily cleared out to store part of the archives of the Reich Security Main Office, moved to Terezín from the bombed-out Berlin. Seen in this light, the Jewish prisoners in the Ghetto served as live shields for the local SS officers, protecting their major records and documents against Allied air-raids. Overcrowding of the Terezín Ghetto was also the reason for resuming transports to the East on September 6, 1943. In a single day 5,007 people left Terezín for Auschwitz II - Birkenau. These prisoners, just like those deported by the following transports, were put there in sector BIIb, where a "Terezín family camp" for Terezín Ghetto inmates had been established.

Meanwhile, the "beautification" campaign in Terezín came to a head. Its consequences were felt in many areas. What were previously known as orders of the day became "Notices from the Jewish Self-Administration", whose letterheads were brightened up with an idyllically conceived drawing of Terezín. The SS Camp headquarters was changed to "SS Office in Terezín". Great attention was paid to face-lifting the houses throughout the town and its green spaces. Flowerbeds were laid out in the main square, and a pavilion where music was regularly played was built in its center. A perfectly furnished children's pavilion, complete with a playground and other attractions, was put up in a nearby park. A former gym was turned into a "community center" offering two halls for cultural programs, a prayer room, a library and a restaurant on a terrace. However, the "beautification" campaign also made it imperative to reduce the number of prisoners in the Ghetto. That was why primarily the sick as well as prisoners whose appearance was not deemed fit to be shown to the foreign visitors were deported to Auschwitz. That was why as many as 5,007 people left Terezín in December 1943, followed by another 7,503 in May 1944. All in all, 17,517 people were deported to the "Terezín family camp" in Auschwitz, of whom only 1,168 survived until the end of the war.

Preparations for the arrival of the foreign delegation culminated in the spring of 1944. Under the supervision of the high-ranking SS officers from Berlin and Prague the delegation's route through Terezín was planned down to the greatest detail, all the activities to be performed by the inmates during the visit had been thoroughly rehearsed as well as replies they were allowed to give to eventual questions from the visitors. In short, this was a well-rehearsed theater performance with the inmates playing the part of involuntary actors under the threat of a death sentence.

The long-prepared visit materialized on June 23, 1944. Its members included the Swiss physician Maurice Rossel, a delegate of the International Committee of the Red Cross, Frants Hvass, an official of the Danish Foreign Ministry, and Eigil Juel Hen-

ningsen, inspector of Denmark's Health Care Service. The delegation was first received at the SS headquarters and then left for the Jewish Self-Administration where the visitors talked with its officials. Then the members of the delegation set out on a sightseeing tour of the town, during which they spoke with some of the inmates and heard their stock answers according to a well-rehearsed script. As a result, the visit – as seen by the SS headquarters – proved to be very satisfactory. The report compiled by Rossel on the visit and the findings thus gained tallied perfectly with the SS needs and expectations. Rossel fell for the SS deception and even went as far as to describe Terezín as a "final-destination camp" from which the Jews were no longer deported. The truth was that by the time his report was finished dozens of thousands of former Terezín prisoners had already been killed in the extermination camps in the East, while death was awaiting many others.

The Nazi propaganda needs were also well served by a documentary shot in Terezín in August and September of 1944. The stage props of a freshly painted and face-lifted town were used to present a fictitious image of what was billed as contented life in a "Jewish settlement territory". Some of the inmates, headed by the world famous director Kurt Gerron, were forced to participate in this farce. The shooting proceeded according to the SS orders. The documentary shows, for instance, a meeting of the Council of Elders, an open-air cabaret, Terezín's café, bank, a performance of the children's opera *Brundibár* in the "community center" as well as a soccer match played in the yard of the Dresden Barracks.

Just a week after the shooting of the propaganda documentary the officials of the Jewish Self-Administration were told by the SS headquarters that because of Terezín's inadequate production capacities, a large number of inmates would have to be sent for labor in the East. One day before the dispatch of the first in a forthcoming wave of transports, Terezín's second Elder of the Jews Paul Eppstein was executed. Almost all the members of the Council of Elders and other officials of the Jewish Self-Administration with their families were sent with the transports. The SS headquarters then cynically offered the women prisoners whose husbands had been deported earlier to leave Terezín and join them in the East. As a result, many women on their own reported for the transports with their children, voluntarily leaving the Ghetto on their way to certain death. A total of 18,402 people left Terezín for Auschwitz between September 28, and October 28, 1944. Only 1,574 of them survived until the end of the war.

It is evident that one of the reasons leading to such a drastic emptying of the Terezín Ghetto and deportation of its inmates in the productive age as well as the officials of the Jewish Self-Administration was an effort to undermine the Ghetto's resistance potential. After all, this is corroborated by a letter sent by Himmler to K. H. Frank, the high-ranking SS and Police Commander and the German Minister of State for Bohemia and Moravia. The letter pointed to the possibility of an uprising breaking out in the Czech lands in the upcoming weeks and to the need of imposing preventive measures and precautions.

After the departure of the last transport to Auschwitz on October 28, 1944, no more than 11,068 prisoners remained in Terezín. This dramatic reduction in its work force had to be made up for by the labor of women, youth and children. The Self-Administration also had a difficult task to get back on its feet, resuming its activities only in December. Benjamin Murmelstein was appointed the new Elder of the Jews, Leo Baeck was head of the Council of Elders.

The difficult situation at the end of 1944 caused fears among the inmates that the Ghetto – or rather the "Jewish settlement territory" as it was called – would be liquidated. That was why they were relieved to hear the news of the arrival of new prisoners from Slovakia. As many as 1,447 Slovak Jews from a camp at Sereď, in the past a regular point of departure of Slovak Jews for Auschwitz II - Birkenau, arrived in four transports to Terezín from December 1944 until April 1945. After the extermination facilities in Auschwitz were closed down, transports had to be rerouted to Terezín. The Slovak Jews also brought the Terezín inmates the news of the actual functioning of the Auschwitz death factory. For those who stayed in Terezín these reports shattered their previous illusions and hopes concerning the fate of their family members, relatives and friends who had been deported to Auschwitz in the past.

In the middle of January 1945 the Reich Security Main Office decided that Jewish spouses of "mixed" marriages from Germany, Austria and the Protectorate of Bohemia and Moravia should be sent to Terezín for what was termed a "guarded labor duty". At that time, "the 'mischlinge' (part-Jews)" from the Protectorate were also deported to the Ghetto. The members of both persecuted minorities were to be imprisoned in the Ghetto with the aim of their la-

bor making up for the reduction in its work force caused by the fall transports. The first transport carrying those prisoners left Prague on January 31, 1945. By the end of April 5,736 people from both categories were deported to Terezín.

Another group of new arrivals included 1,150 Hungarian Jews who had been previously deployed for fortification work near Vienna and who were deported to Terezín in March 1945.

The approaching end of the war and inevitable defeat of Hitler's Germany were causing ever greater nervousness in the SS ranks. Physical liquidation of the Terezín Ghetto inmates still before the arrival of the Allied forces was considered by the SS Camp headquarters as a viable option. A new facility popularly called the "duck pond" was built in one of the fortification moats. This was a compound that could be hermetically closed and used for killing the inmates either by drowning or shooting. A gas chamber was also under construction in part of the Terezín fortifications. But it was never finished. One of the contributory factors was the passive resistance of the prisoners who slowed down and hampered its construction, while their underground resistance organization was getting ready to block the operation of the gas chamber if completed.

But the main reason for these developments was the policy now pursued by Himmler and the Reich Security Main Office Chief Ernst Kaltenbrunner who planned to use Terezín for their own skin-saving designs, as illustrated by Himmler's negotiations with Jean Marie Musy, former Chairman of the Swiss Federal Council, held on January 15, 1945. These talks resulted in the sending of a transport from Terezín to Switzerland. This brought unexpected freedom to 1,200 prisoners who really left for Switzerland on February 5, 1945.

Part of the plans hatched by the top-ranking SS officers to protect themselves and their interests before the end of the war was also the second visit to Terezín to be paid by a delegation of the International Committee of the Red Cross. Following Adolf Eichmann's inspection trip to Terezín in early March 1945, another "beautification" campaign of the town got under way, this time lasting a full month. The local café resumed its services, theater performances and concerts were given, music was again played in the pavilion in the main square.

Arriving in Terezín on April 6, 1945, the second foreign delegation consisted of Otto Lehner and Paul Dunant, representing the International Committee of the Red Cross, and a Swiss diplomat named Buchmüller. After the visit Lehner wrote an enthusiastic report praising the "Jewish settlement territory". Once again this fitted in perfectly with the SS plans. Even though the SS organizers of the "model Ghetto" strategy managed to get away with their deceit again, the fast course of events at the end of the war prevented the Nazis from making any political capital out of their latest propaganda gimmick.

The fast approaching end of the war manifested itself in Terezín ever more clearly. All the inmates saw the departure of the Danish Jews to Sweden in a convoy of Swedish Red Cross buses on April 15, 1945, as an evident signal presaging an early end of their suffering. But there were many other signs of the camp's approaching liberation. Another unusual transport left Terezín on April 24, 1945, this time carrying away mostly the wives and children of the SS officers as well as part of the SS staff. In the next few days, the SS started burning documents from the archives of the Reich Security Main Office. While the prisoners were strictly prohibited to collect charred remnants of the documents flying about in the camp, a special commando supervised by the SS kept collecting the pieces of documents they could lay their hands on.

The war was drawing to a close but the end of suffering and hardships for the Terezín Ghetto's inmates was nowhere in sight. The so-called evacuation transports carrying prisoners from the concentration camps vacated before the advancing Allied armies started arriving in Terezín by train as well as on death marches on foot from April 20, 1945. As a result, more than 15,000 people swelled the Ghetto's population of some 17,500. They arrived in a very miserable state, all starving to death. Many prisoners died on arrival, others lay dead in the trains. These transports brought in mostly Jews from Poland and Hungary, together with prisoners from many other countries. Some 300 of them came to Terezín for the second time during the war. These were the inmates who had been sent to Auschwitz and who were lucky during the notorious selections to be singled out for forced labor. As latter-day slaves they then toiled in various parts of the Nazi-occupied Europe. As a rule, their fellow prisoners who remained in Terezín could hardly recognize them as the new arrivals – just as all the other people brought in by evacuation transports – were returning in a truly deplorable state. Many of them died soon after arrival due to the previous hardship and suffering.

The greatest danger then lurking in the Ghetto was posed by communicable diseases with which the new arrivals were literally infested. These included primarily spotted fever, a disease that exacted a terrible price in Terezín at the very end of the war. Particularly during the arrival of the first evacuation transports efficient quarantine measures to isolate the sick prisoners from healthy ones were virtually impracticable. Exhausted by the hardships of the war, the prisoners hardly realized the imminent dangers of infection. The first spotted fever case was reported on April 24, 1945, after which the infection began to spread like an avalanche. The disease was contracted even by those who had been in Terezín before the arrival of the evacuation transports.

On May 2, 1945, Paul Dunant, a delegate of the International Committee of the Red Cross, arrived and assumed control of Terezín on its behalf. The power of the SS was crumbling very quickly. SS officers were busy burning the remaining documents and the "supermen" who had until recently been the undisputed masters over the life and death of the inmates were now hastily fleeing the town. Most of them left on May 4, followed – one day later – by the last Camp Commander Karl Rahm. Still, not even these developments meant total freedom for the inmates, as the camp was encircled by retreating Wehrmacht and SS units whose shots fired into the Ghetto still exacted more victims. It was only in the late afternoon on May 8, 1945, that the first Red Army units under the command of General I. G. Ziberov, part of the First Ukrainian Front, advancing towards Prague passed through Terezín. On May 10, 1945, the Red Army officially assumed control of Terezín. Major M. A. Kuzmin, who had been appointed commander of the town, got down to organizing food supplies and taking measures necessary to eradicate the spotted fever epidemic. Later on, his No. 1 task was the repatriation of the former prisoners.

There were as many as 29,320 inmates crowded in the town at the end of the war. Some 4,000 people, primarily former inmates from the Czech lands, left the Ghetto on their own during the first days after the liberation, still before a strict quarantine was imposed in the camp following an outbreak of spotted fever.

Already on May 4, 1945, a group of Czech physicians and medical personnel, members of the so-called Czech Action for Help, arrived in Terezín, headed by epidemiologist Karel Raška from Prague who was appointed by the Czech National Council. The typhus fever patients were then, from May 7, being transported from the nearby Gestapo Police

Prison in the Small Fortress to the Ghetto. Quarantine hospitals were set up for those patients in the Sudeten and Bodenbach Barracks. Under these circumstances, vital assistance was also granted by the Soviet Army's Health Service. Between May 11 and 13, a total of 53 Soviet Army physicians and 340 members of its intermediate medical personnel arrived in Terezín. At the order of the high command of the First Ukrainian Front 5 field hospitals with mobile laboratories, delousing stations and showers were also made available. The Soviet health service group in Terezín was commanded by Major L. J. Gerinstein. Still, the brunt of fighting the epidemic had to be borne by the Jewish physicians and medical personnel. Aaron Vedder, an epidemiologist from the Netherlands, was entrusted to coordinate their activities.

The epidemic culminated between May 6 and 16, 1945. Because of possible spread of the infection outside the town, Terezín was hermetically sealed off on May 14, and a fifteen-days quarantine was declared. The sick were isolated in hastily built infection wards in the hospitals and in the aforementioned field hospitals. By that time the patients were receiving adequate care, medicaments as well as enough food. Thanks to these measures the number of new cases began to drop on May 20, and at the end of the month permission could be given to start the repatriation of the former inmates. The Soviet medical personnel left Terezín in June 1945.

The death toll of the spotted fever epidemic as well as other contagious diseases was terribly high. Only during the last few days of the war and the first few weeks of peace 1,566 former inmates died, including 34 Jewish medics. Four members of the medical staff of the Czech Action for Help organization also died while fighting the epidemic, and there were many victims among the Soviet Army health personnel as well.

The whole repatriation process was managed by the Czechoslovak Repatriation Commission which, based in the building of the former SS Camp headquarters, started its work on May 23, 1945. The Franco-Belgian Repatriation Commission and the Commission of the American Joint Distribution Committee also began to operate in Terezín soon afterwards. It comes as no surprise that the first former inmates to leave Terezín were Czechoslovak nationals, later followed by citizens of other countries. Unfortunately, repatriation was being hampered by lack of transport vehicles and fuel. By June 30, 1945, there were still 5,952 people in Terezín.

The liberated camp was kept running mostly thanks to the great devotion of its former inmates. Many of them put off their own departure home by weeks or even months to help their sick and exhausted comrades. On May 11, 1945, Jiří Vogel was appointed head of the camp's Self-Administration. On the same day, the Czech National Council (Parliament) formally abolished the former Ghetto.

As of June 19, 1945 the camp's official name was "Former Concentration Camp, the Municipality of Terezín". All the persons leaving Terezín in the following days and weeks had to undergo stringent medical examinations and luggage disinfecting procedures. Before their departure they were given clothing, food and some money to get home. On arrival in their destinations all the former inmates were obliged to report to local medical authorities to undergo yet another medical examination. The largest groups of former prisoners from abroad – namely Hungarians and Poles – were leaving in the second half of June. But many Polish, German and Austrian Jews refused to be repatriated and asked instead for emigration to North America or Palestine. These people left Terezín as late as in July and August 1945. Citizens of some 30 countries of the world had to be repatriated, including children. Regrettably, there were many orphans among them who were looked after by an organization led by the great humanist Přemysl Pitter. His agency had placed the children in sanatoria and convalescent homes from which they were later sent to different educational institutions.

The Self-Administration of the former concentration camp in Terezín was officially abolished as of August 15, 1945, formally closing the last act in a great drama in the Terezín Ghetto's history. Everyone expected that its epilogue would be the administration of justice over the perpetrators of the crimes committed in the Ghetto. However, most of the SS officers who stayed in Terezín during the war managed to escape their responsibility. Only a fraction of them were captured and brought to trial – by a special people's tribunal at Litoměřice – or to courts abroad. Siegfried Seidl, the first Camp Commander, was arrested and sentenced to death in Austria. His successor Anton Burger twice escaped from prison and died unpunished in the 1990s. Karl Rahm, the third and last Terezín Camp Commander, was sentenced to death by a Litoměřice court. Most of their henchmen were tried and sentenced in absentia or were never brought to court at all. To a large extent, justice has not been dispensed...

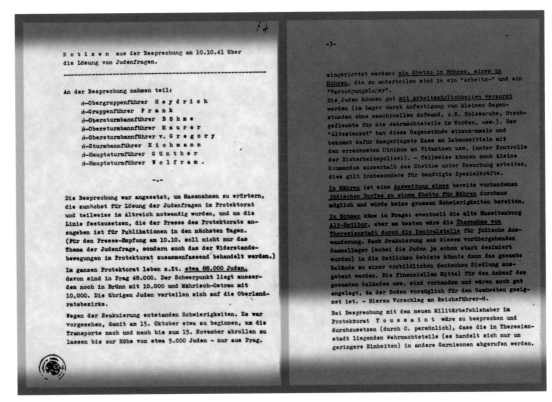

(33) **The arrival of Reinhard Heydrich as the Acting Reich Protector in Bohemia and Moravia brought an acceleration in preparations for the "Final Solution of the Jewish Question" in the Protectorate. That issue was also discussed at one of the first consultative meetings of Heydrich's inner staff on October 10, 1941**

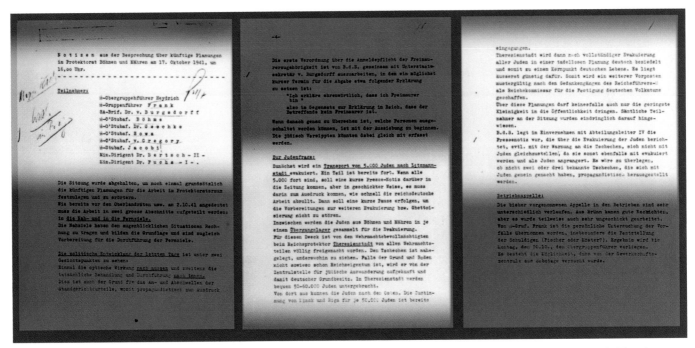

(34) **Another consultative meeting of Heydrich's staff on October 17, 1941, passed the final decision to establish a ghetto in Terezín**

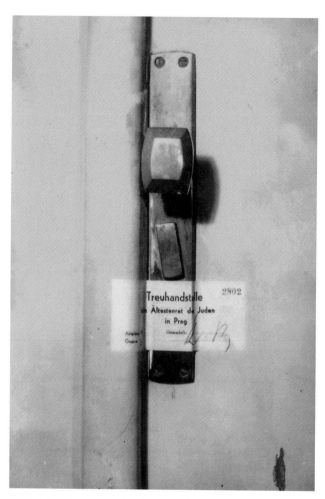

(36) The property stolen from the Jews was concentrated and sorted out. Furniture stored in a synagogue

(35) Apartments of the Jews leaving in transports were confiscated. A sealed Jewish apartment

(37) Leaving the railway station at Bohušovice nad Ohří, people who arrived in the transports had to walk the 2.5 kilometer distance to Terezín on foot. Some of the old and sick people did not survive that journey

(38) The SS headquarters, headed by the Camp Commander, was the actual master over the life and death of the inmates. Members of the SS headquarters in a drawing by Leo Haas

(39) The gallows near Terezín's Aussig Barracks, the site of two mass executions of the Ghetto inmates

(40) Prisoners were interrogated and tortured in the bunkers beneath the SS Camp headquarters

(41) A special unit of the Protectorate gendarmerie was made available to the Terezín SS Camp headquarters for guard and escort duties

(43) Entrance to the so-called Jewish cells in the Small Fortress (current status)

(42) The "offenders" among the Ghetto inmates who had violated the "camp regulations" were often sent to the Gestapo Police Prison in the Small Fortress. A group of prison wardens

(44) The Jewish Self-Administration was established in Terezín just as in the other ghettos and Nazi concentration camps. Its structure was announced in the camp's first order of the day issued on December 15, 1941

(45) Jakob Edelstein, the first of the three Elders of the Jews of the Terezín Ghetto. He was killed in Auschwitz together with his wife and son on June 20, 1944

(46) Paul Eppstein (standing), the second Elder of the Jews, during his address to the Council of Elders. He was shot dead in the Small Fortress on September 27, 1944. Eppstein was replaced by Benjamin Murmelstein (seated on his left)

(47) **Figurines of a girl and a boy leaving in a transport were made in the Ghetto by Erna Bonnová**

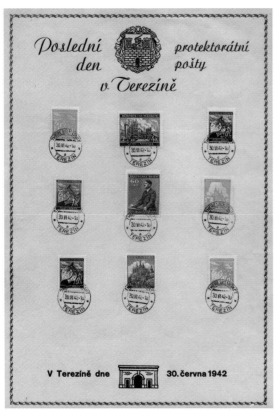

(48) **By mid-1942 Terezín's civilian population was moved out and the whole town was turned into a large jail. A commemorative sheet marking the last day of the Protectorate postal service in Terezín**

(49) A report from the Gestapo office at Würzburg on preparations for transports to be sent to Terezín

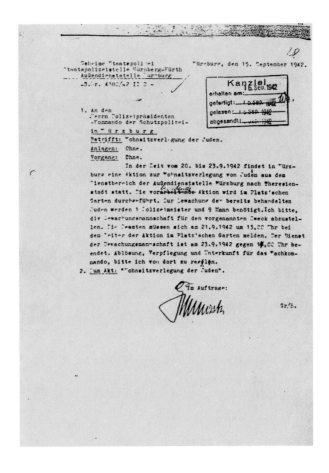

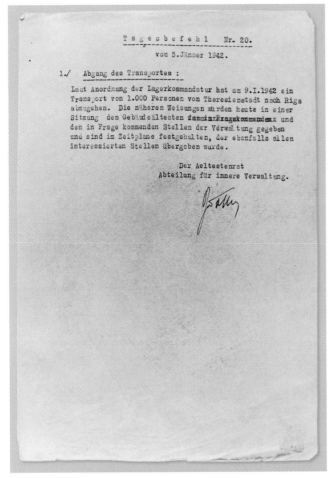

(50) Any hopes cherished by the inmates that Terezín might be their "final-destination camp" were thwarted already on January 5, 1942, when the order of the day announced the first transport to the East

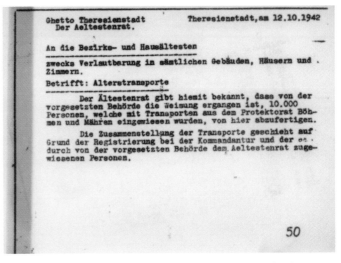

(51) The problem of overcrowding in the Ghetto was solved by its SS Command in the usual way – through deportations to the East. Announcement of the transports of elderly people in October 1942

(52) Starting on June 1, 1943, transports to and from Terezín used a new railway siding built by the Ghetto inmates

(53) After some of the inmates managed to escape from the Ghetto, the SS Camp headquarters ordered a head count. The roll-call in the Bohušovice Basin on November 11, 1943, in a drawing by Leo Haas

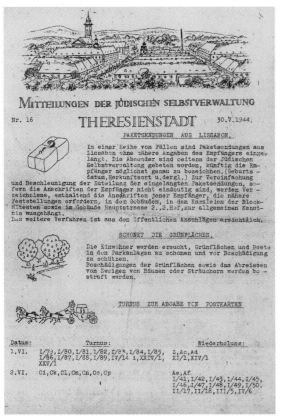

(55) **Alfred Kantor captured in his drawing last-minute preparations for the visit to Terezín paid by a delegation of the International Committee of the Red Cross**

(54) **The SS propaganda "beautification" campaign in Terezín also called for a change of the hitherto used orders of the day to "Notices from the Jewish Self-Administration". Their letterhead was embellished with an idyllic drawing**

(56) **As of May 1943 the Ghetto had its own money which, however, had no real value**

(57) The Nazi propaganda intended to score heavily with its "documentary" made in Terezín. This shot from the film is entitled "In a lecture hall"

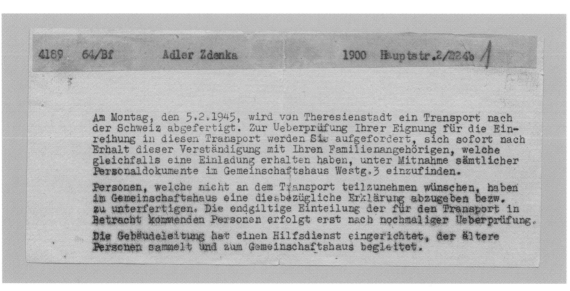

4189   64/Bf   Adler Zdenka   1900   Hauptstr.2/224b

Am Montag, den 5.2.1945, wird von Theresienstadt ein Transport nach der Schweiz abgefertigt. Zur Ueberprüfung Ihrer Eignung für die Einreihung in diesen Transport werden Sie aufgefordert, sich sofort nach Erhalt dieser Verständigung mit Ihren Familienangehörigen, welche gleichfalls eine Einladung erhalten haben, unter Mitnahme sämtlicher Personaldokumente im Gemeinschaftshaus Westg.3 einzufinden.

Personen, welche nicht an dem Transport teilzunehmen wünschen, haben im Gemeinschaftshaus eine diesbezügliche Erklärung abzugeben bezw. zu unterfertigen. Die endgiltige Einteilung der für den Transport in Betracht kommenden Personen erfolgt erst nach nochmaliger Ueberprüfung.

Die Gebäudeleitung hat einen Hilfsdienst eingerichtet, der ältere Personen sammelt und zum Gemeinschaftshaus begleitet.

(58) One of the steps taken by the SS headquarters to save its skin at the end of the war was to give permission to some of the Terezín inmates to leave for Switzerland. A summon for the "Swiss" transport which left the Ghetto on February 5, 1945

(59) The space in front of an unfinished gas chamber built at the end of the war

(60) Documents from the Reich Security Main Office archives, kept in Terezín since the summer of 1943, were burnt in April 1945. Some of the charred documents came into the hands of the Ghetto inmates

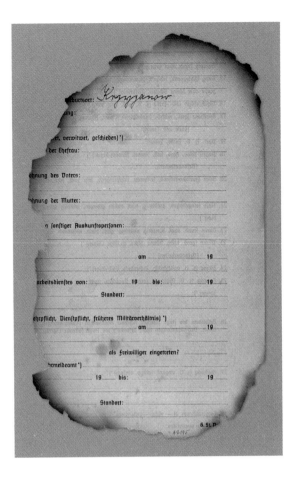

(61) On April 20, 1945, new prisoners began to be brought to Terezín by evacuation transports from other Nazi camps

(62) The first Red Army units passed through Terezín in the afternoon on May 8, 1945

(63) At the end of the war and in the first weeks of peace people in Terezín were still dying in a spotted fever epidemic. A notice board warning against the epidemic

(64) The Jewish orphans who survived the Ghetto were looked after by a charity organization led by the great humanist Přemysl Pitter. This picture shows some of the children in a nursing home at Kamenice near Popovice

(65) A train with former inmates on the Terezín railway siding before departure

(66) SS-Obersturmführer Karl Rahm, the last of the three Terezín Camp Commanders, before his execution on April 30, 1947

HISTORICAL AND DOCUMENTARY
EXHIBITION ON THE SECOND FLOOR

LIFE AND DEATH IN TEREZÍN – THE FACES OF A NORMAL DAY IN GHETTO LIFE

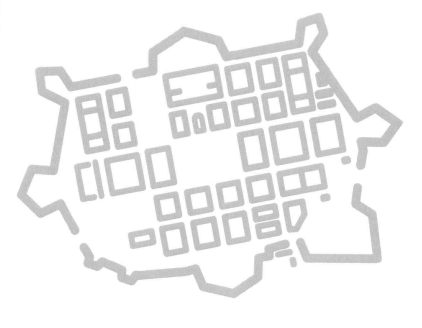

LIFE AND DEATH IN TEREZÍN

The prisoners of the Terezín Ghetto were not only passive victims of the Nazi genocide. The Jewish Self-Administration, physicians and other medical personnel, teachers and educators, workers and technicians, artists and cultural workers as well as the other inmates sought to create more tolerable conditions for their life in the Ghetto so that mutual assistance and solidarity should become natural phenomena among the inmates. They also tried hard to maintain and reinforce their fellow prisoners' physical and mental strength and resistance, stimulating their trust in the future.

However, the "Final Solution of the Jewish Question" could only be prevented through a military defeat of Hitler's Germany. As a matter of record, the resistance movement in the Terezín Ghetto was not strong enough to prevent transports to the East. Yet, its ultimate goal was to slow down and obstruct the decimation of the prisoners by the camp regime directly in Terezín. Three main resistance groups were active in the Ghetto – a Zionist, Czech-Jewish and communist one. All agreed that even their eventual merger would not be sufficient to organize armed resistance. In spite of anticipated heavy loss of life, a mass uprising against the SS troops could and would have materialized solely if the SS headquarters decided to liquidate the Ghetto and its inmates. The members of the local resistance groups, who could only rely on weapons and explosives to be seized in an eventual successful ambush of SS officers, had only a limited amount of petrol and some tools they planned to use as weapons.

The resistance cells in the Ghetto sought to maintain contact with the outside world, their members keeping the other inmates informed about developments on the fronts and trying to dispel feelings of hopelessness and solitude among the prisoners. They also organized escapes by some of the inmates who – when free – often joined the anti-Nazi resistance units active in the Protectorate. For instance, after his escape from the Terezín Ghetto Karel Körper joined a resistance unit in the Plzeň region and in Prague. He later fought in the Slovak National Uprising where he died in action. Another 20 Terezín escapees later fought in other partisan groups. But, generally speaking, the key principle of the Ghetto's resistance movement was that each member should work primarily among his fellow prisoners in the camp, or wherever he might be deported from Terezín.

(67) **Karel Körper (1919–1944), who had fled from a Terezín inmates' labor gang working in the Oslavany mines, then fought in the Czech resistance movement, later joining the Slovak National Uprising. He was killed in action on November 12, 1944**

(68) **An illegally made radio receiver, built into a suitcase, was used by the Ghetto inmates to listen to radio news on the developments in World War II battlefields**

LIFE AND DEATH IN TEREZÍN

One of the most depressing aspects of life in the Ghetto was an absolute shortage of space in its dormitories. Overcrowding led to the loss of the last remnants of privacy, resulting in great mental stress of the inmates, a contributory factor to the spread of various diseases and psychic deprivation. Before the war Terezín was inhabited by some 7,500 people, its military garrison included. When the Ghetto's prison population reached its peak in September 1942, as many as 58,491 men, women and children were crowded within its walls. As a result, space formerly intended for a single person had to accommodate more than 8 people. In 1942, the average floor space per one inmate amounted to a mere 1.65 square meter, in March 1943 this was slightly over 2 square meters. This intolerable situation was invariably solved by the SS Camp headquarters in the same way – by deporting the Terezín inmates to death camps or slave labor. Thus the accommodation standards in the Ghetto slightly improved at the terrible cost of the death of tens of thousands of people. In the summer of 1944 one inmate had at his or her disposal floor space covering 3.05 square meters.

The inmates of the Terezín Ghetto were accommodated in its former army barracks (in actual fact, its Sudeten Barracks alone housed many more prisoners than the town's total civilian population before World War II). They also lived in civilian houses evacuated by their former tenants till the middle of 1942, in newly built timber barracks as well as in many different makeshift dwellings – sheds in yards, casemates and especially in the attics of different objects. For instance, in October 1942 as many as 6,034 people were crammed in overcrowded attics, often sleeping on bare floor or on their own suitcases.

Living in the barracks as well as in former civilian houses, the prisoners usually slept in three-level bunk beds, set close to one another. These were just 65 centimeters wide, the clearance between each level was 80 centimeters, making it virtually impossible for the inmates of normal height to sit upright in bed. At the same time, each bunk bed was the only "private living space" the prisoners ever had in the Ghetto. However, the real scourge of the dormitories and other sleeping quarters was the ever-present vermin as well as mice and rats which contributed to the rapid spread of contagious diseases.

Needless to say, these intolerable conditions posed major sanitary problems affecting the inmates' most fundamental vital needs. Especially during the first period of the Ghetto's existence such problems were compounded by a desperate shortage of water. There was a catastrophic dearth of wells, washrooms, toilets and sewerage in the Ghetto. People had to stand in endless lines everywhere. The already difficult situation was further exacerbated by the SS Command's repeated bans on lighting as a cruel collective retribution for the smallest individual misdemeanor.

The never-ending fight with vermin, contagious diseases but also physical deprivation caused by prolonged lack of privacy formed a depressing background to everyday life in the Ghetto.

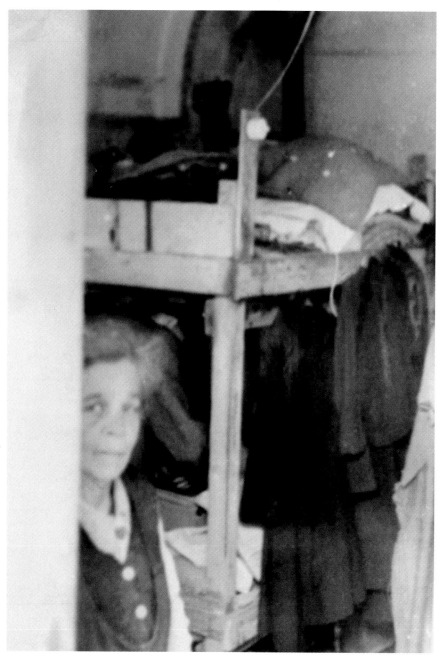

(69) Woman prisoner and her "home"

(70) František Mořic Nágl: Prison sleeping quarters

(71) **Ferdinand Bloch: Sleeping quarters in the loft**

(72) **Men's sleeping quarters in the Hannover Barracks**

LIFE AND DEATH IN TEREZÍN

Hunger experienced by the Terezín Ghetto prisoners most frequently manifested itself as long-term malnutrition, caused not only by the meager – absolutely insufficient – food portions served to the inmates but also by the inadequate nutritional value of the food, its utter uniformity and dire lack of vitamins. Last but not least, food was often served cold, while people had to stand in long and degrading lines to get it.

It is next to impossible to give an accurate and credible picture of the actual extent of starvation in the Ghetto. For understandable reasons, the official SS statistics and documents were falsified. As a result of the lack of fats and proteins in their diet the inmates were quickly losing weight.

Low-quality bread was the only staple diet in the Ghetto. Initially, the daily bread ration was 250 grams, increased to 350 grams a day in December 1943. By the end of the war, the short ration amounted to 700 grams of bread per head once in 4 days. Moreover, considerable differences existed in the rations provided to the different groups of prisoners, classified into several catering categories. People working in physically demanding manual jobs received somewhat larger food portions, those who did not work at all were given less than the low average. Children had somewhat better food, getting extra helpings because they were regarded as the hopes for the future. Of course provided they survived...

Those inmates who had relatives and friends outside the Ghetto could occasionally receive food parcels. A precondition for receiving a food parcel was the so-called "permission" stamp that could only be obtained in precisely stipulated terms. That had to be sent to the benefactor living outside the Ghetto. But, to be honest, the number of people to whom such stamps could be sent was rapidly diminishing.

On the whole, the nutritional value of the food served to the Terezín Ghetto inmates was invariably very bad, figuring among the main factors contributing to the systematic decimation of the prison population.

(73) **Jan Tomáš Spitz: A crowd waiting for food**

(74) Jiří Schubert: Scraping scraps of food from casks, 1943

(76) A special voucher for waste vegetables. Good-quality vegetables grown in the local gardens were either supplied to the SS kitchen or to customers outside the Ghetto

(75) Leo Haas: An old woman waiting for food, 1943

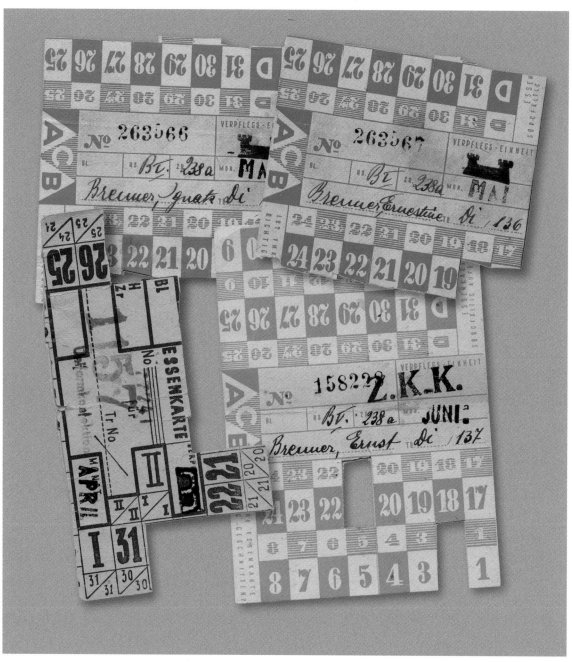

(77) **Prisoners' food vouchers**

DYING AND DEATH

One of the key functions of the Terezín Ghetto was the decimation of its Jewish population. Even though the methods used towards this end differed in many respects from those employed in the Nazi extermination camps, as many as 33,818 people perished in the Ghetto due to physical and mental suffering or in various epidemics. This was almost one quarter of all the prisoners who had passed through the Ghetto, not including the victims of the so-called evacuation transports at the end of the war. The latter started arriving in Terezín on April 20, 1945, and the death-rate among their members was very high indeed.

After the whole town of Terezín was turned into a huge concentration camp, its Central Mortuary was built in parts of its former casemates. Dead bodies were kept there and prepared for burial. Two Ceremonial Halls designed for simple ceremonies were built in the adjoining sector. During the time of peak mortality rate in the Ghetto mass funeral services were held several times a day, attended by family members, relatives and friends of the deceased who were allowed to pray and pay their last respects. One room was reserved for Jewish rite ceremonies, the other for Christian funerals as many Christians, classified as Jews according to the Nuremberg Laws, were also deported to Terezín.

People were buried in the Jewish Cemetery built in the Bohušovice Basin behind the town, initially into individual graves, but very soon solely into mass graves. Mourners and friends were allowed to pay their last respects to the deceased at the walls of the Ghetto. Then the coffins would be taken out of the Ghetto. But the growing death-rate in the camp made it necessary to speed up the construction of a local crematorium. When finished, four of its incineration ovens were gradually launched into operation, starting on September 7, 1942. The crematorium also housed a dissecting room.

In the early days of the Ghetto, the ashes of the deceased were put into wooden funeral urns but soon afterwards paper cinerary ones, manufactured in the Ghetto's cardboard workshop, began to be used. These were placed in the Columbarium, inaccessible to the inmates. That was established in part of the casemates opposite the Central Mortuary. With the approaching end of the war the Nazis tried hard to cover up all the traces of their horrible crimes. That was also why the ashes of many thousands of their victims had to disappear. In November 1944, the SS Camp headquarters ordered part of the ashes to be thrown into the river Ohře beyond the walls of the Ghetto, the rest to be buried in a pit near the concentration camp in the nearby town of Litoměřice.

(78) **Karel Fleischmann: Sick women
in the attic of L 504, 1943**

(79) **Ferdinand Bloch: A burial service**

(81) Karel Fleischmann: Paying last respects in the mortuary, 1943

Toten-Fusszettel.

Name

Vorname   Trp. Nr.

Sterbeort: Haus

        Zimmer

Sterbetag

Sterbestunde

Totenbeschau am

        durch

Der Leichenbeschauer

A12-50.000-17.X.42-U.G.R. 277

(80) A tag tied to the leg of dead bodies in the Ghetto

(82) Some of the inmates regarded suicide as a way out of their hopeless situation. The Jewish Self-Administration prepared a table with charts showing the number of suicides, attempted suicides as well as the suicide methods used up to the end of 1943

SELBSTMORDE u. SELBSTMORDVERSUCHE in THERESIENSTADT vom 24.XI.1941 bis 31.XII.1943.

	XI	XII	I	II	III	IV	V	VI	VII	VIII	IX	X	XI	XII	I	II	III	IV	V	VI	VII	VIII	IX	X	XI	XII	Σ
SELBSTMORDVERSUCHE	-	2	2	3	3	1	6	25	45	82	60	14	20		43	24	15	16	5	7	9	9	15	6	5	10	430
MÄNNER	-	2	-	-	2	1	1	1	6	19	27	16	4	8	14	9	6	3	4	2	4	3	1	1	2	3	139
FRAUEN	-	-	2	3	1	2	-	5	19	26	55	44	10	12	29	15	9	13	1	5	5	6	14	5	3	7	291
TÖDLICH VERLIEFEN:	-	-	1	2	3	3	1	5	21	25	54	35	9	12	27	12	9	15	4	2	3	2	2	1	-	4	252
MÄNNER	-	-	-	-	2	1	1	1	5	10	20	8	3	6	9	6	5	3	3	1	-	-	-	-	1		88
FRAUEN	-	-	1	2	1	2	-	4	16	15	34	27	6	6	18	6	4	12	1	2	-	1	2	1	-	3	164
PROTEKTORAT	-	2	2	3	3	3	1	3	4	6	9	31	2	2	13	5	4	3	2	4	1	4	11	4	2	5	129
REICH	-	-	-	-	-	-	-	3	21	39	73	29	12	18	30	19	11	13	3	3	8	5	4	2	3	5	301
GIFT	-	-	2	2	2	1	-	4	21	31	52	41	9	12	29	13	9	10	1	4	6	7	15	5	4	5	285
SCHNITTWUNDEN	-	1	-	-	-	-	-	2	4	14	8	4	2		8	5	4	3	3	-	3	2	-	1	-		65
ABSTURZ	-	1	-	1	1	2	1	2	-	4	11	5	-	1	3	3	1	1	1	3	-	-	-	-	-	4	45
ERHÄNGEN	-	-	-	-	-	-	-	2	6	5	6	1	5		3	3	1	2	-	-	-	-	-	-	1	-	35

1942   1943

SELBSTMORDVERSUCHE HIEVON ■ TÖDLICH

REICH / PROTEKTORAT — NACH HERKUNFT

SELBSTMORD-VERSUCHE DURCH: ☐ GIFT ☐ SCHNITTWUNDEN ☐ ABSTURZ ☐ ERHÄNGEN — 285 65 45 35

TABELLE

(83) Karel Fleischmann: Loading coffins on a flatbed, 1943

(84) Bedřich Fritta: Army uniform repair shop

(85) Prisoner Doris Schimmerlingová grazing sheep

(86) Construction of barracks for a mica splitting operation and export production

LIFE AND DEATH IN TEREZÍN

Even though the Terezín Ghetto was not a labor camp, labor conscription was officially imposed for all the inmates aged between 16 and 60. As a matter of fact, even younger and older prisoners had to work as well. Working hours usually amounted from 52 to 54 hours a week, in November 1944 the norm was raised to 70 hours. The prisoners assigned to work and especially those doing hard manual jobs received somewhat higher food portions than people unable to work. Wages in Ghetto currency were introduced in 1943 but the local money had no purchasing power. Indeed, this was a sheer formality, part of the SS strategy to paint a distorted picture of what the Nazis claimed to be a "Jewish settlement territory".

First and foremost, the inmates had to work to ensure the camp's basic functions, its accommodation and catering capacities, provisioning, health care, operation of its water mains, electricity and sewerage. They also worked to cater for the needs of the SS and to meet the deliveries for various companies outside the Ghetto. Haberdashery, cardboard and other goods were produced for those customers.

War production was not very significant in the Terezín Ghetto. Its biggest operation was splitting mica for insulation in electric devices. Wehrmacht uniforms were also repaired in the Ghetto's workshops. Part of the workshops, concentrated in the so-called Bauhof, was set aside solely for the needs of the SS. For less than a year, the Ghetto was also responsible for what was called "K-production" (Kistenproduktion), a code-name for the manufacture of boxes serving as protective covers for devices starting engines in winter. There were also two joiner's workshops working on orders for the German army.

The Ghetto's agricultural business, catering mostly for the SS and Wehrmacht needs, was also relatively large, including livestock production. At the end of the war, its livestock included 30 horses, 70 heads of cattle, 250 sheep, goats and pigs and over 800 pieces of poultry.

At the order of the SS the inmates had to build a crematorium, an almost 3-kilometer long railway siding connecting Terezín with Bohušovice nad Ohří, and a new road bypassing the Ghetto around its outskirts. Three new Artesian wells were sunk, almost one kilometer of new water mains was laid and a 1.5-kilometer sewerage network was also built.

Prisoners were also sent in labor gangs to work outside Terezín, in the mines, forests, on building sites, and in road construction and repair. The biggest of these labor gangs, consisting of 200–250 men plus several women, worked on the construction of barracks for the SS at Wulkow near Berlin between March 4, 1944, and February 3, 1945. Some 1,000 women prisoners from Terezín worked in the Křivoklát forests in 1942, other inmates were assigned to work in the Kladno and Oslavany mines, at the chateau of Heydrich's widow at Panenské Břežany and elsewhere.

For a time, such slave labor conscription guaranteed that the prisoners involved were exempted from deportation to the extermination camps in the East. However, even this temporary advantage definitely disappeared in the fall of 1944.

(87) An unknown author depicted in his drawing the Wulkow camp where a Terezín labor gang worked

(88) A labor gang from Terezín also worked at Panenské Břežany, in the home of Heydrich's widow

70

(89) **The work card of Leo Kollinský who worked in the Ghetto's agricultural sector**

(90) **Otto Ungar: Building the railway siding, 1943**

(91) Doctor Erich Munk was in charge of the Healthcare Department of the Jewish Self-Administration. In October 1944 he was deported to Auschwitz where he perished

(92) Norbert Troller: Surgery in the Ghetto, 1943

(93) Karel Fleischmann: Dormitory for blind women, 1943

LIFE AND DEATH IN TEREZÍN

The healthcare system, built in the Ghetto by the Jewish Self-Administration, came into being under incredibly harsh circumstances. The number of patients who needed medical care kept steadily rising. Transports were bringing in seriously ill people whose health required immediate treatment. Due to the appalling accommodation and hygienic conditions, many healthy inmates soon contracted various diseases. Especially in the early days of the Ghetto's existence its surgeons and medical personnel had to perform even the most complicated surgeries with the most primitive instruments, hampered by constant shortages of medicaments and dressing material. Water shortages were also quite common, making it impossible to comply with the basic hygienic requirements. There were frequent power cuts as well so that many operations had to be performed in candle light. The overall situation improved very slowly indeed. Only after the Ghetto's medical services could use part of the inventory confiscated from Jewish doctors, was it possible to furnish the specialized hospital wards in Terezín as well as its network of consulting and treatment rooms. Still, critical shortages of medicaments and sanitary material remained a common occurrence.

All in all, 225 specialists, 256 general practitioners and 68 dentists worked in the Ghetto in February 1943. Terezín's medical services gradually succeeded in establishing a relatively dense network of healthcare facilities, staffed by a number of outstanding specialists deported to Terezín from different European countries. It should be stressed, however, that the medical personnel themselves were prisoners as well, suffering just as much as their patients and other Ghetto inmates.

An important task facing the medical services in the Terezín Ghetto was to prevent the outbreak of major epidemics, while paying considerable attention to strict compliance with basic hygienic norms and requirements, and to vermin eradication. The Self-Administration worked very hard to build a central disinfecting station, while disinfecting teams were busy regularly delousing the barracks.

A particularly critical situation was faced by invalids among the inmates who were dependent on the help of their fellow prisoners. The SS headquarters approached the problem of "treating" patients suffering from tuberculosis and mental illnesses by sending them in transports to the East, thus passing a virtual death sentence over such people. There were several thousand disabled people, mostly World War I invalids, and hundreds of permanently handicapped inmates (there were 4,000 invalids, 1,100 deaf-and-dumb and 600 blind inmates at the end of 1943) in the Ghetto.

Despite the dedicated efforts of the local medical personnel the sickness rate in the Ghetto was still very high, mostly due to prolonged starvation, mental stress, physical exhaustion and overcrowding. That was why typhus, scarlet fever and intestinal catarrh epidemics broke out every now and then, while various other diseases caused by malnutrition and vitamin deficiency also spread throughout the Ghetto. Due to the inmates' generally impaired health, even children's diseases were rife among the Ghetto's adult population, often with fatal consequences. Despite the wholehearted efforts on the part of its medical personnel, who often worked to total exhaustion, the deplorable health situation in Terezín could only be slightly improved but its high mortality rate could hardly be radically reduced. As a result, dying and death proved to be a daily occurrence in the Ghetto, the fear of contracting diseases and dying accompanying each prisoner at every step.

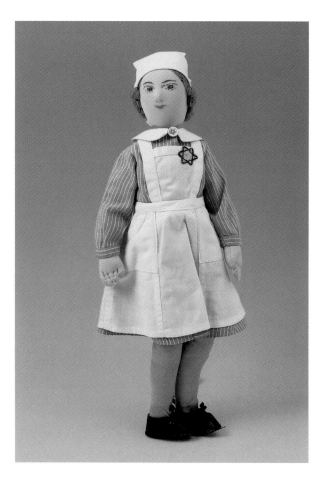

(94) **Figurine of a nurse made by woman prisoner Erna Bonnová**

(95) **Leo Haas: In the Terezín hospital, August 4, 1943**

74

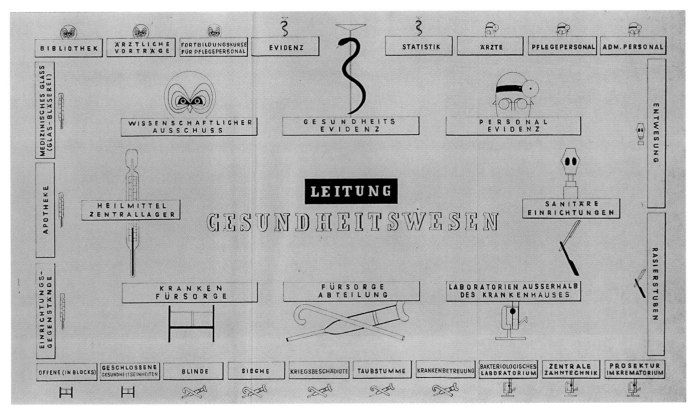

(96) A chart illustrating the Ghetto's healthcare system in a report on the activities of the Jewish Self-Administration for 1942, prepared for the SS headquarters

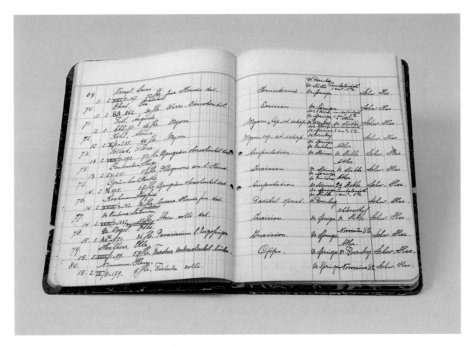

(97) A book of surgical operations performed in the Ghetto.
Entries for February 11–15, 1945

(98) **Alfred Bergel: Library in the Ghetto, November 27, 1943**

(100) **A selection of drawings and documents on display on a round panel in the exhibition hall. This comes from a large corpus of documents collected by Karel Heřman who survived his imprisonment in the Terezín Ghetto**

(99) **Verdi's *Requiem* rehearsed with a choir and orchestra by Rafael Schächter. Performed in the Ghetto on many occasions, this composition had symbolic importance for the inmates, expressing their confidence in their future freedom**

CULTURE GAVE STRENGTH

The cultural life in the Terezín Ghetto flourished to a truly exceptional degree. There were many outstanding professional artists as well as amateurs among the dozens of thousands of its inmates. Initially, the SS headquarters only tolerated their cultural activities but later on – in an effort to exploit Terezín for their own propaganda aims – the Nazis gave the Jewish Self-Administration a relatively free hand in this area.

Developing from what were originally called "comradely evenings" (Kameradschaftsabende), first allowed by the SS at the end of December 1941, the Ghetto's cultural life grew both in size and in quality, encompassing not only privately pursued fine art activities, such as drawing, painting or sculpting, and literary work but also various public performances – concerts, opera and drama performances, cabarets as well as a rich program of lectures. An irreplaceable role in Terezín's cultural life was played by its libraries, mostly consisting of books brought into the Ghetto by the prisoners themselves.

Cultural events were held at various places – in cellars, attics, yards or directly in prisoners' barracks. In organizational terms, all the cultural activities were arranged by the Leisure Time Department (Freizeitgestaltung), which concentrated the artists and prepared a whole gamut of cultural activities. An opportunity to perform in public was thus offered to budding artists and amateurs alike. Terezín's cultural performances had their dedicated and grateful protagonists as well as devoted audiences. In this way, dozens of thousands of people, forced to live in such degrading conditions and in constant fear of deportations, could strengthen their spirit, dignity and integrity.

Major works of art as well as minor – purely entertaining genre-pieces were created in Terezín. A common denominator of all the cultural events in the Ghetto was a dedicated effort to boost the morale and spirit of the author as well as his audiences, instill optimism and promote trust in a better future. Many cultural programs carried distinct allegorical and symbolic overtones, reflecting an undercurrent of spiritual resistance. Some of the performances were not eventually staged in public because of fears of subsequent reprisals by the SS Camp headquarters. It was realized that the authors of such works had evidently ridiculed their torturers. A case in point was Viktor Ullmann's opera *Der Kaiser von Atlantis oder die Tod-Verweigerung* (The Emperor of Atlantis or Death Resigns) composed to the libretto by Petr Kien or Karel Švenk's play *Poslední cyklista aneb Bořivoj a Mánička* (The Last Cyclist or Bořivoj and Mánička).

But the inmates easily recognized similar symbolism also in other works, for instance in the children's opera *Brundibár* composed by Hans Krása to a libretto by Adolf Hoffmeister. The opera's final chorus celebrating the victory over a mean old hurdy-gurdy man became the unofficial anthem of the Ghetto. Another unforgettable cultural experience in the Ghetto was each performance of Verdi's *Requiem*, rehearsed by the conductor Rafael Schächter. There were many other musical performances as well as drama and cabaret productions which were noted for similar inherent symbolism and hidden messages.

Many outstanding artists deported to the Terezín Ghetto eventually succeeded in elevating the standards of its cultural life to a truly exceptional level. In addition to personalities mentioned above, this applies to such distinguished musicians as, for instance, composers Gideon Klein and Pavel Haas, conductors Franz Eugen Klein, Karel Ančerl, Egon Ledeč and Karel Taube, and singers Karel Berman, Heda Grab-Kernmayr and Marion Podolierová.

As for theater performances in Terezín, Gustav Schorsch, Carl Meinhard, Norbert Frýd (Nora Fried), Zdeněk Jelínek and Vlasta Schönová figured among the main organizers of Czech- and German-language theater in the Ghetto. An excellent stage-designing background to such performances was provided primarily by František Zelenka. Terezín's cabarets, whose leading personalities included Karel Švenk, Kurt Gerron, Hans Hoffer and Leo Strauss, were also known for their very high artistic standards.

Fine arts occupied pride of place in the Ghetto's cultural life. After their official work in the Drafting Room of the Jewish Self-Administration's Technical

Office, the local painters had an opportunity to capture in their unofficial and clandestine works the genuine face of everyday life in the Ghetto. Bedřich Fritta, Karel Fleischmann, Leo Haas, Otto Ungar, Ferdinand Bloch, Petr Kien and many other artists created works of art that spoke volumes about wartime Terezín. These are not only accomplished and valuable works of art but also unique documents tracing the history of the Ghetto.

Literary work in the Czech language was represented in Terezín by such writers as Otto Weiss and Karel Poláček. Camill Hoffmann, Ilse Weber and Walter Lindenbaum should definitely be mentioned among the leading German writers living in the Ghetto. Countless poems, short stories and other prose writings as well as satirical works written in Terezín will remain anonymous for ever. They were either destroyed or their authors perished during the war.

Quite surprisingly, the censorship practiced by the SS Camp headquarters was comparatively mild. In addition to the aforementioned propaganda goals pursued by the Nazis, the reason for such a lenient approach was the fact that all the prisoners were regarded as doomed to death anyway. That was why their cultural pursuits were tolerated by the SS as a safety valve helping maintain order in the Ghetto until the last transport to the East. Indeed, Eastern transports proved to be the biggest enemies of art and culture in the Ghetto. With ruthless regularity they carried away performing artists as well as their audiences to an unknown destiny. That was why many performances had to be canceled or rehearsed time and again with new performing artists. But that was also another side of the rich cultural life in the Terezín Ghetto.

(102) **A souvenir poster for Gogol's play** *Ženitba* **(The Marriage). The stage and costume designer for the Terezín performances was František Zelenka. He died during a transport to Auschwitz in October 1944**

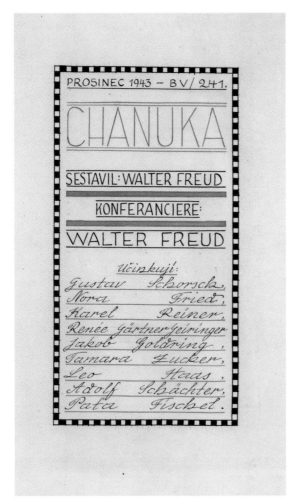

(101) **Culture and arts in Terezín also helped in reviving the Jewish religious traditions. A souvenir poster marking the feast of Hanukkah in 1943**

(103) **Carl Meinhard was a leading representative of the German theater life in the Ghetto. A poster for the play** *Der Erfolg des Kolumbus* **(The Success of Columbus) directed by Meinhard**

(104) **Kurt Gerron was the best-known author of the German-language cabaret in Terezín. A souvenir poster for his cabaret** *Karussel* **(Carousel)**

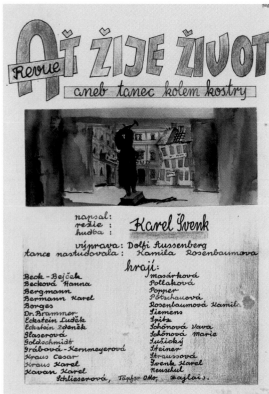

(105) **One of the most popular Czech cabaret performances in the Ghetto was a revue called** *Ať žije život* **(Long Live Life), written by Karel Švenk**

(106) Leo Haas: Cabaret in a yard

(107) Tickets for a cultural performance in the Ghetto

(108) **Richard Feder, the rabbi of Kolín**

שמע ישראל יהוה אלהינו יהוה אחד ואהבת את
יהוה אלהיך בכל לבבך ובכל נפשך ובכל מאדך והיו
הדברים האלה אשר אנכי מצוך היום על לבבך ושננתם
לבניך ודברת בם בשבתך בביתך ובלכתך בדרך
ובשכבך ובקומך וקשרתם לאות על ידך והיו לטטפת
בין עיניך וכתבתם על מזזות ביתך ובשעריך
והיה אם שמע תשמעו אל מצותי אשר אנכי
מצוה אתכם היום לאהבה את יהוה אלהיכם ולעבדו
בכל לבבכם ובכל נפשכם ונתתי מטר ארצכם בעתו
יורה ומלקוש ואספת דגנך ותירשך ויצהרך ונתתי
עשב בשדך לבהמתך ואכלת ושבעת השמרו לכם
פן יפתה לבבכם וסרתם ועבדתם אלהים אחרים
והשתחויתם להם וחרה אף יהוה בכם ועצר את
השמים ולא יהיה מטר והאדמה לא תתן את יבולה
ואבדתם מהרה מעל הארץ הטבה אשר יהוה נתן לכם
ושמתם את דברי אלה על לבבכם ועל נפשכם וקשרתם
אתם לאות על ידכם והיו לטוטפת בין עיניכם ולמדתם
אתם את בניכם לדבר בם בשבתך בביתך ובלכתך
בדרך ובשכבך ובקומך וכתבתם על מזוזות ביתך
ובשעריך למען ירבו ימיכם וימי בניכם על האדמה
אשר נשבע יהוה לאבתיכם לתת להם כימי השמים
על הארץ

(109) **The manuscript of a Jewish prayer from the Terezín Ghetto**

SPIRITUAL LIFE

Of truly exceptional importance for boosting the prisoners' morale, mental strength, composure and will to survive was, quite definitely, their religious life and opportunity to attend divine services and other ceremonies, although these were mostly held in the Ghetto's makeshift conditions. In addition to Jewish believers, also many Christians who had been classified as Jews under the Nuremberg Laws were deported to Terezín. In actual fact, the Nazi definition of Jewishness prioritized mainly membership of Jewish religious communities of not only the person concerned but also of his or her parents and grandparents. The share of Christians in the Ghetto's prison population soared at the end of the war, as "Jewish spouses of mixed marriages" and "mischlinge (part-Jews)" were sent to Terezín.

Despite this fact, no serious conflicts caused by different religious convictions and beliefs were registered among the inmates. What is more, all the Ghetto survivors agree that it would be hard to find a more religiously tolerant community than that in Terezín. Prayer rooms were set up in cellars, attics, former garages, warehouses or sheds, and in many cases a single prayer room was shared by people of different religions.

Still, the bulk of believers in Terezín professed the Jewish belief, which was eventually also espoused by many of the inmates who had originally been atheists or non-practicing believers. The tragic war-time experience led many Jews to their religious belief as their only hope. The famous rabbis imprisoned in the Ghetto, including Leo Baeck, the rabbi of Berlin, Richard Feder, the rabbi of the Czech town of Kolín, or Max Friediger from Denmark were also acknowledged religious authorities.

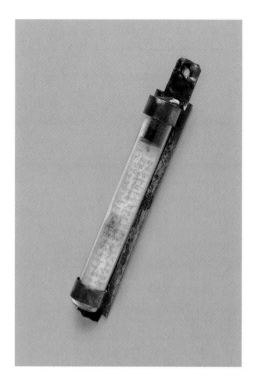

(110) **A mezuzah (a case with a Jewish prayer) from the Terezín Ghetto**

(111) **Figurine of a rabbi made in the Ghetto by Petr Kien**

(112) **Ferdinand Bloch: Services in the loft**

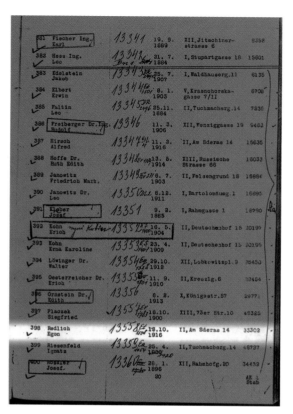

(113) **Egon Redlich in a photograph taken during his studies**

(114) **Part of the Ak/St transport list with Egon Redlich's name**

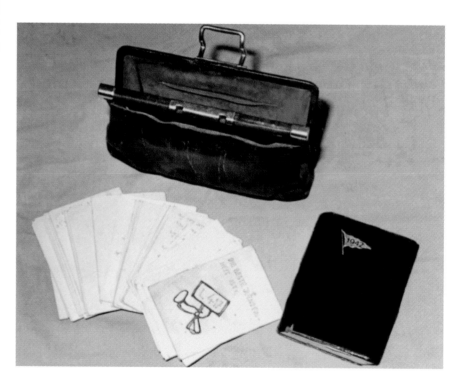

(115) **Redlich's diary was found on February 14, 1967, during repairs of the roof of the house in Dlouhá Street No. 15. The diary together with a handbag in which it was hidden**

86

ONE IN TENS OF THOUSANDS

No single exhibition can shed light on the individual fate of each of the tens of thousands of people who had passed through the Terezín Ghetto. That was why one particular prisoner has been selected so that his destiny could illustrate what really lies behind the strict official statistics and the spine-chilling figures on deportees and deaths in the Ghetto. In the eyes of the proponents and organizers of the "Final Solution of the Jewish Question" their victims were nothing but statistical figures. However, a particular live person, a specific human life destroyed by the Nazis should be seen behind each such figure.

Egon Redlich was born in Olomouc on October 13, 1916. He studied law at Prague's Charles University until the Nazi occupation of the Czech lands in 1939 brought his university studies to an abrupt end. As an ardent supporter of the Zionist movement, Redlich systematically prepared himself for post-war life in Palestine where he hoped to emigrate. He was deported to Terezín as early as on December 4, 1941. Redlich was appointed a member of the Council of Elders and head of the Children and Youth Care Department in charge of their upbringing. In actual fact, he was involved in organizing their clandestine education. In this particular capacity he did his best to popularize the cause of Zionism among the young people in the Ghetto. In keeping with the Zionist principles he tried to integrate upbringing with the educational system of children and youth.

Redlich figured among the leading personalities of the cultural life in the Ghetto, actively participating in its various cultural programs. While in Terezín he even wrote a stage play. From his arrival in the camp until his deportation to Auschwitz he kept writing a diary in Czech and Hebrew, thus leaving behind one of the most important evidence on the history of the Terezín Ghetto, on the Zionist movement among its inmates, and on the life and education of its children and youth.

On October 23, 1944, Egon Redlich, together with his wife and their six-month old son, was deported to death in the Auschwitz gas chambers.

(116) **Old Jews in the German town of Hanau before boarding a transport train**

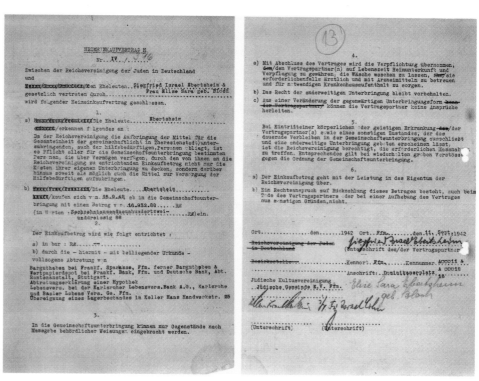

(117) **One of the fraudulent contracts on the "home purchase" the Jews of Germany were forced to conclude**

LIFE AND DEATH IN TEREZÍN

The living conditions of elderly people in Terezín, who were often ill and unable to look after themselves, were mostly shocking, to say the least. Much more than other categories of inmates elderly people suffered from the lack of basic hygiene and frequently inaccessible medical care. Unable to work, elderly prisoners also received small portions of food, and therefore experienced permanent hunger.

The largest group of elderly people in Terezín was formed by prisoners from Germany and Austria. Proceeding from the conclusions of the notorious Wannsee Conference, also the German and Austrian Jews over 65 years of age began to be deported to Terezín en masse. Soon enough, the elderly people from Germany and Austria outnumbered those from the Protectorate of Bohemia and Moravia deported to Terezín before them. Accommodation in such makeshift dwellings as attics, casemates, stables etc., without basic sanitary installations brought to such people much greater suffering and hardships than to their younger fellow prisoners. To make things worse, unlike their contemporaries from the Protectorate old people from Germany and Austria had no younger relatives and friends in the Ghetto who could give them a helping hand, either in physical and psychic or emotional terms. These people were also shocked by the fact that under the promise of life-long accommodation and the provision of medical and other types of care they had con-

cluded before their departure for Terezín what were called contracts on the purchase of homes. Such contracts usually cost them all their property, which was then seized by the SS.

Thus cheated, these elderly people were arriving absolutely unprepared to face Terezín's cruel reality. Deeply traumatized, most of them could not cope with the hunger, diseases and other hardships of the camp life. That was why death-rate in this particular age group was especially high. Therefore, even though in the summer and fall of 1942 the overall share of prisoners older than 65 years ranged between 46 and 50 percent of the total prison population, their overall number was fast declining due to the reasons given above. Another reason for that was the deportation of elderly people to the extermination camps in the East. In this way, the SS headquarters decided to tackle the problem of the overcrowded Ghetto and to avert the danger of contagious diseases. Seen in this light, the time during which Terezín could justifiably be called a ghetto for the elderly ended after approximately six months. Those elderly people who stayed in Terezín represented the most deplorable and wretched category of prisoners, although the Jewish Self-Administration went out of its way to alleviate their plight by establishing elderly people's homes that provided basic care and organized various types of assistance.

(118) **Elderly women waiting for food, 1942**

The miserable existence of the Ghetto's elderly inmates, as depicted in Karel Fleischmann's Terezín drawings

(119) **An elderly woman lying down**

90

THE YOUNGEST PRISONERS

Children had to share the bitter experience of living in Terezín with the adult inmates. The Ghetto's Self-Administration was known to be trying to create for them at least slightly more tolerable conditions in accommodation, catering and overall care. That was the task of its Youth Care Department (Jugendfürsorge). Beginning in the summer of 1942, many homes for children and youth were established in Terezín, then turned into a large prison. These homes concentrated most of the youngest prisoners, led by assigned educators and teachers who looked after their all-round mental and physical development and purposeful use of their free time. That was why daily programs in the homes included cultural, sports but also educational activities. Many outstanding teachers, such as Valtr Eisinger, Růžena Engländerová, Josef Stiassny, Willi Groag, Egon Redlich and Fredy Hirsch, were involved in educating the young people, organizing clandestine school lessons, debates and cultural programs attended by the leading personalities of prewar science, arts and political life. On the whole, some 55 to 60 percent of the Ghetto's children lived in the homes, the rest staying with their mothers, older boys with their fathers in sleeping quarters. These children too were looked after by the Jewish Self-Administration's Youth Care Department.

The Terezín educators did their utmost to instill in the children a sense of discipline and order, trying to strengthen their character and bring them up for a better life after the war. Quite understandably, in their world-view education they proceeded from their own philosophy. There were three fundamental trends in youth education applied concurrently in the Ghetto: namely the Zionist, communist and Czech-Jewish ones, the last mentioned espousing and applying the principles of President Masaryk's concept of democracy.

The teachers and educators in the homes organized clandestine classes in the main school subjects. Despite the very primitive conditions in which tuition was held, on the whole the children mastered an exceptionally broad body of knowledge, a solid basis for further education, even though only for those precious few children and youth who lived to see the end of the war.

The environment of the Ghetto, into which the youngest prisoners were suddenly thrown, led many of them to a desire to express their emotions and thoughts in writing. This gave rise to poems and various other literary forms which today vividly reflect the atmosphere in the life in the Ghetto as well as the basic facts from its development. These literary works by young authors were generally noted for exceptionally mature content and form, possibly due to the fact that in the Ghetto the children matured very quickly and soon began to see the world through the eyes of their adult fellow prisoners. This literary production was presented primarily on the pages of magazines produced in a single copy or just in several copies. The most famous of these magazines was "Vedem" published by boys in the building L 417. Out of all the young writers active in the Ghetto, mention should be made at least of the two great talents: Petr Ginz and Hanuš Hachenburg. The painter and teacher Friedl Dicker-Brandeisová gave art classes – the only form of education not banned by the SS – during which the children made drawings reflecting their feelings, aspirations and fantasy as well as depicting their memories of home.

Of special importance for the youngest inmates of the Terezín Ghetto was the children's opera *Brundibár*, played fifty five times with the enthusiastic participation of young actors and to great applause of their audiences. Both understood very well the message of the opera that expressed faith in the final victory of good over evil.

(120) **Valtr Eisinger, head of the boys' home No. 1 in the building L 417. In September 1944 he was deported to Auschwitz where he perished**

(121) **Academic painter Friedl Dicker-Brandeisová. She was deported to Auschwitz in October 1944 where she also perished**

(122) **Records of the Youth Care Department of the Jewish Self-Administration on the number of children in the Ghetto as of September 12, 1943**

(124) "Poupata" (Blossoms), a primer used in Czech elementary schools, happened to be found while Terezín's civilian population was moving out of the town. The book was later used during clandestine lessons in the Ghetto

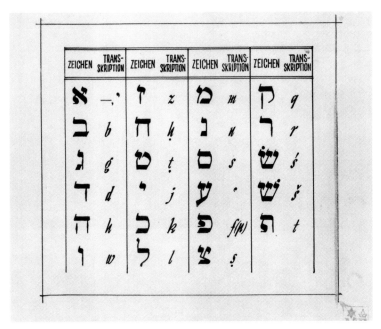

(123) The children and youth in the Ghetto were keen on learning Hebrew. A teaching aid used in the Ghetto

(125) A souvenir poster for the performance of the play *Broučci* (The Beetles)

(126) **Performance of the children's opera** *Brundibár*. **A photograph from a Nazi propaganda documentary**

(127) **Boys living in the youth home in the Hamburg Barracks published a magazine called "Domov" (Home)**

THEY SPOKE DIFFERENT LANGUAGES

The Jewish prisoners were deported to Terezín primarily from the countries of Central and Eastern Europe. The members of the individual communities differed only in what people of various countries differ in general – their language, customs, cultural traditions, religion, and mentality. The SS Camp headquarters went out of its way to foment conflicts between the individual groups of prisoners from different countries, trying to divide them in an effort to control the whole captive community better. But those endeavors yielded only modest results. Throughout the existence of the Ghetto, togetherness, cooperation, solidarity and mutual understanding remained the main factors of coexistence among the inmates from different countries.

Approximately one half of the Ghetto's prison population were Jews from the Protectorate (73,594). This was due to the original specification of the camp as well as its geographic position. People from this group of prisoners were also strongly represented in the Jewish Self-Administration not only due to the size of their group but also because they had been in the Ghetto from its very beginning.

The second most numerous group were Jews from Germany (42,219), followed by Austrian Jews (15,274). Quite large was the group of the Jews deported from the Netherlands (4,897) out of whom more than a half were Jews coming from Germany anyway. The Danish Jews (466) formed a small group of inmates who, however, enjoyed an exceptional position in Terezín. Because of the peculiarities of Nazi Germany's occupation policies in Denmark as well as the strong positions assumed by Danish authorities and an overwhelming part of that country's general public, the Jews from Denmark were protected from deportations to the Nazi extermination camps and from slave labor. The Ghetto population comprised a relatively small group of Jews from the German-occupied Czech border regions (612).

The Jews from Slovakia (1,447) began to arrive in Terezín as late as in December 1944 after the Auschwitz camp, the main destination of Slovak Jews until then, went into liquidation. And the Slovak Jews were the first to bring to Terezín reports on the real functioning of the Auschwitz "death factory" and on the genuine fate of the relatives and friends of the Terezín inmates who had been deported to Auschwitz by previous transports.

The last large group of Terezín Ghetto prisoners arrived in March 1945 from Hungary (1,150) via Vienna where these people had been working on the fortifications in the vicinity of that town.

Beginning on April 20, 1945, some 15,397 additional prisoners from many countries came pouring into Terezín in the so-called evacuation transports and on death marches from different concentration camps and their subsidiary camps vacated before the approaching Allied armies.

(128) **The Jews assembled before leaving for their transport train (picture from Plzeň)**

(129) **Jews from the Netherlands were imprisoned in the Westerbork camp (pictured here) before deportation to Terezín**

(130) **Slovak Jews on their way to a transport**

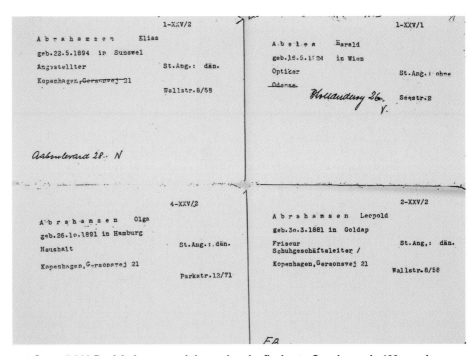

(131) **Some 7,200 Danish Jews saved themselves by fleeing to Sweden, only 466 people were deported to Terezín. Index cards with the names of the Danish Jews in the Terezín Ghetto**

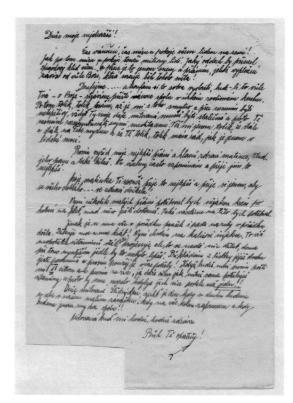

(132) Besides using the legal postal service, the Terezín Ghetto inmates also resorted to exploiting clandestine correspondence channels.
A secret message smuggled out of the Ghetto

(133) A postcard sent from the Ghetto

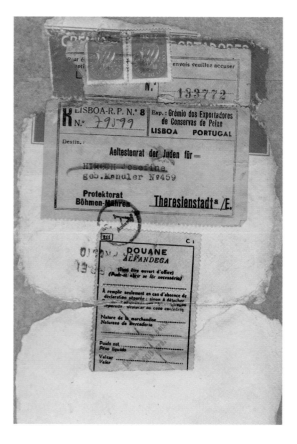

(134) A dispatch note and label on one of the International Red Cross consignments sent to the Terezín Ghetto

WHAT THE WORLD KNEW
ABOUT TEREZÍN

The SS Camp headquarters in Terezín went out of its way to prevent news on the situation in the Ghetto from leaking out. The truth about the real character and purpose of the Ghetto, especially if it happened to reach foreign countries, would spell the end of Nazi attempts at using Terezín for their propaganda goals, and their efforts to conceal the genuine aim of the "Final Solution of the Jewish Question". On the other hand, the Nazis could hardly afford to sever the Ghetto's postal contacts with the outside world outright because of the SS maneuvering to save its skin before the approaching end of the war. That was why inmates' correspondence, originally totally banned, was later allowed in strictly stipulated intervals, although it was heavily censored. The rules guiding Terezín's postal connection with the outside world were drafted personally by Adolf Eichmann.

Following the major reverse of fortunes on World War II battlefields, in the spring of 1943 the SS allowed food parcels to be sent to the Ghetto from abroad. This measure was introduced thanks to the good offices of the Czechoslovak government-in-exile, the International Red Cross, the international Jewish organizations and other charity and assistance organizations. Still, large portions of incoming food parcels were seized by SS officers.

The visits to Terezín paid by delegations of the International Committee of the Red Cross in June 1944 and in April 1945 did nothing to make the international public more aware of the real situation in the Ghetto. On the contrary, the reports compiled by the members of the two delegations served the propaganda purposes of Hitler's Germany very well indeed. Truthful information on the Terezín Ghetto and primarily on the fate of the transports leaving for Auschwitz from October 1942 onwards was brought only by prisoners who had managed to escape from the hell of the Auschwitz camp.

Each escape attempt posed formidable risks, representing a truly heroic act. One of those who succeeded in escaping from Auschwitz was the former Terezín Ghetto inmate Vítězslav Lederer. He even managed to return unobserved to Terezín to inform some of the inmates about the real fate of the Terezín transports in Auschwitz. Strangely enough, most of the Terezín inmates refused to believe Lederer's reports.

There were other prisoners who also managed to escape from the Nazi concentration and labor camps to which they had been deported either directly from Terezín or later sent as slave laborers having passed the infamous selections in Auschwitz.

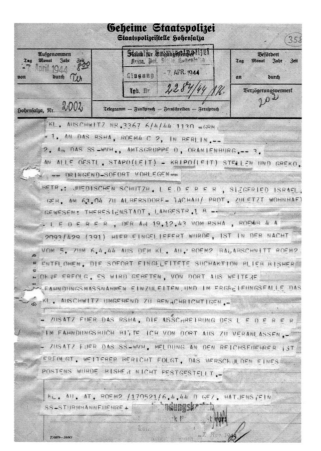

(135) In April 1944 the Auschwitz Camp Command notified all the Gestapo and criminal police stations of the escape of Vítězslav Lederer who had been deported to Auschwitz from Terezín

(136) A false identification card used by the former Terezín prisoner Vítězslav Lederer after his escape from Auschwitz

A DAY IN THE LIFE OF A TEREZÍN PRISONER

Diary entries written by the children and adult prisoners reflect – in quite a unique manner – the life in the Terezín Ghetto, the feelings and impressions of those who found themselves in the grips of the sinister machinery called the "Final Solution of the Jewish Question". The following short excerpts from the memories of 9 inmates are presented at the exhibition in 12 different parts, classified according to individual subjects. Each excerpt is always marked by the author's initials:

RB – Ruth Brösslerová, born on May 19, 1929, in Terezín from January 1942, survived

HP – Helga Pollak-Kinsky, born on May 28, 1930, in Terezín from January 1943, survived

MK – Michael Kraus, born on June 28, 1930, in Terezín from December 1942, survived

WM – Willy Mahler, born on November 3, 1909, in Terezín from June 1942, perished

EM – Eva Mändlová-Roubíčková, born on July 16, 1921, in Terezín from December 1941, survived

ER – Egon Redlich, born on October 13, 1916, in Terezín from December 1941, perished

PW – Pavel Weiner, born on November 13, 1931, in Terezín from May 1942, survived

ChW – Charlota Weinstein-Verešová, born on December 13, 1928, in Terezín from March 1943, survived

HW – Helga Weissová-Hošková, born on November 10, 1929, in Terezín from December 1941, survived

Noxious bugs, cold or extreme heat

... každý dostal jeden díl matrace, příjemné na spaní to není... zima, hlad, prostě k zoufání... nikde pomoc, nikde východisko... (...everyone got one mattress, not too comfortable to sleep on...cold, hunger, enough to drive you to despair, ...help nowhere, no way out...) EM

... Die Kinder kamen um drei Uhr früh. Sie sind voller Läuse. Sie haben nur, was sie am Körper tragen. Wir sammeln Sachen für sie... (...Children arrived at 3 in the morning. They're full of lice. The only things they have is what they have on. We're collecting things for them...) HP

... Nynější stav, kdy štěnice zaplavily naše ubikace a donutily osazenstvo spát na dvorech, na chodbách apod., je neudržitelný... (...The current state of affairs, with bedbugs infesting our sleeping quarters and forcing inmates to sleep in the courtyards, hallways, etc., is unsustainable...) WM

... Schon dem zweiten Tag schlafe ich wegen Wanzen auf dem Gang. Alle sind wir zerbissen... (...I've slept in the hallway for three days now because of the bedbugs. Everyone's covered with bites...) HP

... V blocích lidé pomalu umrzávají, zejména na půdách, kde není vůbec možnost topení. Při dvaceti stupních pod nulou byli již nalezeni zmrzlí lidé... jeden člověk leží na druhém... (...People are slowly freezing to death in the blocks, especially in the lofts where there's no heat. At twenty degrees below zero people have already been found frozen... people lying on one another...) EM

Lack of water and insufficient hygienic facilities

... Von 27 Kinder hatten 19 Durchfall, und 16 liegen krank in Bett. Zwei Aborte für 100 Kinder sind nicht genug, wenn in jedem "Heim" ein infektiöser Durchfall wütet... (...Out of 27 children, 19 have diarrhea and 16 of them are in bed sick. Two toilets for 100 children is not enough when infectious diarrhea is on the rampage in every "home"...) HP

... V seznamu vyreklamovaných zbylo jedno dítě... zemřelo. Starci a stařenky jsou v kasárnách bez záchodů a bez umýváren... (...One child remained on the rejection list... he died. Old folks don't have toilets or sinks in their barracks...) ER

… Dnes se jdu umýt pod pumpu, jelikož se umývárna spravuje… (…I'm going to wash myself at the pump today since the sink is being fixed…) PW

… starci nemají ani místo ani klid, aby mohli zemřít. Nebude možno používat záchodů, protože je ucpáno odtokové potrubí… (…there's not even room or quiet for old people to die. The toilets aren't going to be usable because the drainage pipes are clogged…) ER

… blokové domy s jejich špínou, kde leží jeden nemocný úplavicí na druhém, kde mrtvoly a ti, kteří jsou téměř mrtvolami, leží po celé dni stlačeni vedle sebe, kde matrace se rozkládají vlhkostí a nemohou být vyměněny, takže pod nimi se nacházejí červi… (…filthy block buildings where one person with dysentery lies on top of another, where corpses and those who are practically corpses lie cramped up on one another all day long, where maggots hide under rotting mattresses that can't be replaced…) EM

Unbearably overpopulated Ghetto

… Včera přišli sirotci z Frankfurtu nad Mohanem. Téměř jsme nevěděli, kam je umístit… (…Orphans came from Frankfurt am Main yesterday. We didn't know where to put them…) ER

… Das ist angeblich ein Musterghetto, warum schicken sie also Leute fort, besonders die Alten, vielleicht weil es nicht schön ausschauen würde, wenn man sehen könnte, wie sie um diese widerliche Suppe betteln? Die Stadt ist überfüllt… (…If this is a model ghetto like they say, why do they send people away, especially the elderly? Perhaps because it would make a bad impression if someone saw them begging for that disgusting soup? The town is overpopulated…) ChW

… Jedna matka, která má spalničky, leží se svými dětmi, které jsou také nemocné. Ženy, které odešly se svými dětmi do nemocnice, se vracejí, aniž by našly své místo, které obsadili jiní. Zemřel čtrnáctiletý chlapec… (…One mother is down with the measles and her children are sick, too. Women that go with their children to the hospital come back only to find their spots taken by others. A 14-year old boy died…) ER

… Místnosti jsou plné lidí, výkaly, nedostatek jídelních příborů, mrtví leží mezi živými i celý den… (…Rooms are full of people, excrement, not enough eating utensils, the dead lie among the living for entire days…) ER

… staří lidé padali jako mouchy, protože to po čtrnáctihodinovém stání nemohli již vydržet… (…old people are dropping like flies because they couldn't take it anymore after standing for 14 hours…) EM

Hard labor. Children taught in secret

… Přijel transport z Plzně. Mnoho známých. Přijeli starci (jedna devadesátiletá žena), nemocní a pouze nemnoho schopných pracovat… (…A transport arrived from Pilsen. A lot of acquaintances. Those that came are old {one 90-year old woman}, sick, and only a few are capable of working…) ER

… Zřizují se zde nové produkce na válečnou potřebu. Jsme donuceni jim pomáhat… (…They're starting to produce things needed for the war here. We're being forced to help them. …) RB

… Pracovali jsme v noci… Odnesli jsme jednu mrtvolu z domu do kasáren… Leží zde nyní mrtvoly mezi živými lidmi… (…We worked during the night…. We took one body from the building to the barracks…. Now there are corpses lying here among the living…) ER

… Již více jak 14 dnů pracuje pilně celé krejčovské oddělení na opravách tisíců a tisíců součástí uniforem německých vojínů. Po provedených opravách jsou tyto uniformy připravovány na zimu bílým nátěrem na jedné straně oděvů… (…The entire tailor's department has been working diligently for more than 14 days now on repairing thousands and thousands of uniforms for German servicemen. Once repaired, uniforms are painted white on one side to make them ready for winter…) WM

… První hodinu máme jako vždy profesora Eisingera na češtinu. Probíráme české obrození Josefa II. … (…Like always, our first class is Czech with Professor Eisinger. We're discussing the Czech Revival under the reign of Joseph II…) PW

Lack of food, hunger

… Lidé tě prosí o polévku. Polévku, která je jen teplou vodou, člověk, který dostává balíky, tuto polévku nebere… (…People ask you for soup. Soup that's nothing but warm water. People who get packages don't eat the soup…) ER

... Wir bekommen nur jeden dritten Tag ein Kilogram Brot... Manchmal bekommen wir auch schimmliges Brot und das ist schlecht. Wir schneiden die schimmlige Stellen ab und müssen den Rest dann in ganz dünne Schnitten schneiden, damit es länger reichen soll... (...We only get a kilogram of bread every third day... Sometimes we even get moldy bread, which is bad. We slice off the moldy parts and then have to slice the rest into really thin slices to make it last longer...) ChW

... Vidí-li, jak zde lidé žebrají o kousky chleba po ubikacích, jak prosí o odpadky jídla u kuchyní a výdejen, jak prosí o uschování slupek od brambor a jak po těch almužnách lapají svými zhubenělými rukami... (...Does he see people here begging for pieces of bread in the dormitories, asking for scraps from the kitchens and distribution centers, asking for potato peel to be saved, and grasping for these alms with their emaciated hands...) WM

... Chléb byl v poslední době ztuchlý. Člověk si zvykne na všechno: také na odpuzující a strašné věci... (...The bread's been stale recently. You get used to everything, even repugnant and ghastly things...) ER

... Bída těchto starých Němců je nepředstavitelná. Jdou celý den od pokoje na pokoj a žebrají o kousek chleba... (...The privation of these elderly Germans is inconceivable. All day long they go from room to room begging for pieces of bread...) EM

Tremendous relief – a package of food

... To si nedovedete představit. Jíst na porcelánovém talíři, pít ze šálku a jíst takové dorty a keksy... (...It's inconceivable. Eating off a porcelain plate, drinking from a cup and eating all kind of cakes and cookies...) RB

... Den končil tím, že tatínek otevřel první a poslední sardinkovou konzervu... (...The day ended by dad opening the first and last can of sardines...) RB

... Dostala jsem dnes velký balík z Brna od Rosenzweigů. Je to od nich velmi hezké. Jsou to vlastně skoro cizí lidé. Bylo tam bohužel málo na vaření... (...I got a big package today from the Rosenzweigs in Brno. It's really nice of them since they're practically strangers. Unfortunately there wasn't much in it to eat...) RB

... Jsou zastaveny balíky, prý jich bude povoleno jen dva tisíce za měsíc, tolik, jako dosud za den. Kdo chtěl, mohl vyplnit formulář, na kterém stálo, že jmenovaný žádá o známku pro dotyčného, který mu má balík poslat. Je to dvojsečná zbraň. Máme uvést někoho v Praze? Přesně se jménem a adresou? Nezpůsobíme mu tím nepříjemnosti, protože má spojení se Židy? ... (...Packages have been suspended. They say only 2,000 of them will be allowed per month, which is as many as were allowed up until now per day. Anyone who wanted could fill out a form that said he was requesting a stamp for someone to send him a package. It's a two-edged sword. Should we list someone from Prague? With their name and address? If we do, will we cause them problems for having ties with Jews? ...) EM

... Přišel mi dnes balík z Kyjova, byl sice vykradený, ale bylo v něm hodně... (...I got a package today from Kyjov. Even though it had been opened, there was still a lot in it...) RB

Disinfection meant frequent moves

... s maminkou máme 1,20 m2. V noci leží lidé i na prostředku, jde-li někdo ven, musí je přeskakovat, strkáme jedna druhé nohy do obličeje... (...mom and I have 1.2 m2. At night people also sleep on the floor, so if someone goes outside they have to jump over them, everyone has someone else's feet in their face...) HW

... jsou v byty přeměněny i bývalé chlívečky a pro obydlí přizpůsobeny i částečně volné prostory různých průchodů, spojujících jednotlivé dvory a domy... (...old pigsties are being turned into living quarters and even partially unused areas in walkways connecting courtyards and buildings are fashioned into places to live...) WM

... Tam byly poměry poněkud lepší, neboť to byly opravdu pokoje a ne půdy. V pokoji 6,5 m2 bylo nás tenkrát 21 hochů s jedním opatrovníkem... (...The conditions there were somewhat better since they were real rooms and not lofts. In a 6.5 m2 room there were 21 of us boys and one guardian...) MK

... Stěhování Hamburku... Během 24 hodin přestěhovat 4 tisíce lidí se všemi zavazadly... (...Moving Hamburg... To move 4,000 people and all their luggage in 24 hours...) HW

... Skoro 7000 mužů se stěhuje během 2 dnů. Velká akce. Stěhování malého města, rychle, bez konfliktů. Stěhují lidi a strkají je k 37 000 ostatním... (...Almost 7,000 men are being moved in two days. A major event. Moving a small town, quickly, without conflict. They're moving people and sticking them in with 37,000 others...) ER

A fourth of Terezín's prisoners died

... V noci umřela v předsíni velmi nemocná paní. Měla cukrovku... (...A really sick lady died during the night in the entryway. She had diabetes...) RB

... Maminka je velmi nemocná. Jeden den měla přes 40°, pak hrozný průjem. Má to zde téměř každý. Je to druh úplavice. Zeslabuje to zejména srdce... (...Mother is quite ill. One day she had a fever of over 40°, then terrible diarrhea. Almost everyone here does. It's a kind of dysentery. It particularly weakens the heart...) EM

... Jsem celý den u tatínka, je nemocen. Půjde asi do nemocnice, má stále vysoké horečky... Dnes konečně po dlouhém běhání dostala maminka tatínka do nemocnice L 124. Zjistili, že má zánět pohrudnice s exudátem... (...I've been with dad all day. He's sick. He'll have to go to the hospital since he keeps running high fevers... After running about, mom finally got dad to hospital L 124 today. They found out he has pleurisy with exudate...) RB

... Alenka je na spále, má ji velmi těžkou. K tomu záškrt, zánět středního ucha, spalničky a průjem. Lékařka řekla, že neví, zdali to přežije... (...Alenka has quite severe scarlet fever. Not to mention diphtheria, a middle ear infection, measles and diarrhea. The doctor said she doesn't know if she'll survive ...) RB

... Lilky sestra zemřela. Lilka sama má tyfus. Věra, Olina a Marta šly na marodku... (...Lilka's sister died. Lilka herself has typhus. Věra, Olina and Marta went to the sickbay...) HW

A constant threat – transports

... Odsud pojede transport do Polska. Budeme v něm? Je to příšerné. Myslely jsme, že aspoň před tím zde budeme zabezpečeny, nyní jsme na tom stejně, jako v Praze. Odpoledne byli poslední povoláni a příští den ráno museli již být připraveni... (...A transport's leaving for Poland. Will we be in it? It's terrible. We thought we'd at least be safe from that here, but now we're in the same boat as in Prague. The last ones were called in the afternoon and had to be ready by the next morning...) EM

... Uvnitř Mysliveckých kasáren se schovávali lidé pod postelemi, za postelemi, pod prkny na záchodech, celé rodiny, které prostě nenastoupily, když byly vyvolány a zdánlivě se jim to daří... (...People in the Borderer Barracks were hiding under beds, behind beds, under boards in the bathrooms. Entire families that just didn't go when they were called. They seem to be doing alright...) EM

... Je v tom celý sirotčinec... Pomáhala jsem ve šlojsce u dětí z L 318. Některé neumí ještě pořádně ani mluvit, dvou až tříleté, s transportními čísly kolem krku a tužkou připsáno Waisenkind... (...There's an entire orphanage there... I helped at the sluice with children from L 318. Some of them still don't even know how to talk properly, two or three years old, with transport numbers around their necks and "Waisenkind" written in pencil...) HW

... Odpoledne se bude roznášet transport, 1500 příslušníků těch, kteří odjeli. Ale vždyť jim přece slíbili, že budou jejich rodiny chráněny... (...A transport is going to be passed out this afternoon. 1,500 family members of the ones who left. But I thought they promised them their families would be protected...) HW

... Gestern half ich einer Familie mit sieben Kindern und heute mit drei, deren Mutter Tuberkulose hatte... (...Yesterday I helped a family with seven children and today another family with three children whose mother has tuberculosis...) ChW

Art and culture meant freedom in bondage

... A zase kontrast, možný jen v Terezíně, v ghettu. Sál – vpředu na jevišti zkouška na Wolkerovu „Nemocnici" – vzadu modlící se Židé... (...Another contrast possible only in the Terezín Ghetto. Auditorium: rehearsal of Wolker's "Nemocnice" {Hospital} on the stage in the front and praying Jews in the back...) ER

... Včera jsem byla na Hubičce. I když se zpívá jen za doprovodu klavíru, bez kostýmů a bez kulis, dojem v Národním divadle by nemohl být větší... (...We went to see "Hubička" {The Kiss} yesterday. Even though the singing is only accompanied by a piano and there are no costumes or props, the impression in the National Theater couldn't be more grand...) HW

... Večer nám Magda přichystala překvapení. Přišel k nám pan prof. Eisinger a zpíval nám 3 písně. Byla jsem nadšena... (...Magda surprised us tonight. Professor Eisinger came to visit and sang us three songs. I was ecstatic...) RB

... Denně jsou zde koncerty, přednášky, divadlo, dokonce revue. A současně zde umírají němečtí Židé v blokových domech hlady... (...Every day there are concerts, lectures, plays and even shows here. At the same time, German Jews are starving to death here in the block buildings...) EM

... Odpoledne mám lístek na klavírní sólo Gideona Kleina. Hrál Beethovena, Mozarta, Chopina. Byla jsem unesena... (...I have a ticket for Gideon Klein's piano solo this afternoon. He played Beethoven, Mozart, Chopin. I was captivated...) RB

Do's and don'ts

... Devět lidí, zavřených pro pašování dopisů, bylo pověšeno. Rozsudek museli vykonat Židé. Všude zoufalství... (...Nine people locked up for smuggling letters were hung. The sentence had to be carried out by Jews. Desperation everywhere...) EM

... Opět deset lidí popraveno. Část pro pašování dopisů, někteří, protože se vzepřeli, když je Seidl tloukl. Opět všude hrozná nálada... (...Another ten people executed. Some of them for smuggling letters and some for resisting when Seidl beat them. Spirits are low again everywhere...) EM

... V neděli a pondělí nesměl vůbec nikdo na ulici, pouze na propustku. Od čtvrtka do pondělka byl tento trest v platnosti... (...Only those who had a pass could go out into the streets on Sunday and Monday. This punishment was in effect from Thursday to Monday...) EM

... Tři mladí hoši utekli. Máme za to už týden "Kasernensperre a Lichtsperre", chodíme v kolonách do práce... (...Three young boys ran away. Because of that we've had "Kasernensperre and Lichtsperre" for a week and have to go to work in columns...) HW

... Rodičům, kteří očekávají narození děcka, bylo nyní sděleno, že musí být děcko operativně před narozením odejmuto, nebo po narození utraceno... (...Parents expecting babies were just told they would have to be removed before birth or "put to sleep" after being born...) WM

... Bylo nám dovoleno každému jednou za měsíc 30 slov napsat... (...Everyone's allowed to write 30 words a month...) RB

Hoping for the war to end

... Rok 1942 se chýlí ke konci a s posledním jeho dnem zaplavuje naše srdce a mysle otázka: Přinese nový rok 1943 zakončení současné války? ... Ghetto očekává nový rok s největšími nadějemi. Při tom lidé bydlí na půdách a v tmavých koutech, po zemi a ve sklepích... vcházíme do nového roku 1943 se zapěním naší české hymny "Kde domov můj"... (...1942's coming to an end and our hearts and minds are flooded on the last day of the year with the question: Will new year 1943 bring an end to the war? ... The ghetto has high expectations for the New Year. Even though people are living in lofts and dark corners, on the ground and in cellars... we're welcoming in new year 1943 by singing the Czech national anthem "Kde domov můj"...) WM

... Kdy půjdeme domů? To je heslo Terezína... Jak bude vypadat vítězství? ... (...When are we going home? That's Terezín's motto...What will victory be like? ...) RB

... První věc, co si koupím, bude klavír. Pak si půjdu koupit nové šaty a prádlo a boty podle mého vkusu... (...The first thing I'm going to buy is a piano. Then I'm going to buy new clothes and underwear and shoes the way I like them...) RB

... Jen nebýt nemocný a zůstat zdravý, až přijde konec. Budeme doufat, že přijde v krátké době... (...Just not to be sick and be healthy when it's over. We're hoping it'll be over soon...) ER

... Jak ráda bych chodila s napráskanou aktovkou. Již bych nebyla líná ráno vstávat... Teď by nás mohl zachránit jen konec. Vždyť jednou musí přijít vysvobození. To nemůže věčně trvat... Udělaly jsme si malou oslavu. Vzpomněly jsme na T. G. Masaryka... Jak bychom všechny potřebovaly nějaký nový 28. říjen. Kdy už nám zavlaje prapor svobody a míru? ... (...How glad I'd be to have a cram-packed briefcase. I wouldn't be lazy about getting up anymore... Only the end can save us now. We have to be liberated at some point. This can't go on forever... We had a little party. We thought of T. G. Masaryk... We could all use another October 28. When will the standard of liberty and peace finally wave over us? ...) RB

(137) **Heap of human remains in Majdanek**

OTHER FATES OF DEPORTEES

For a large majority of its prisoners Terezín was just a transit camp from which transports were leaving for unknown destinations. In actual fact, they headed to the German-occupied territories in Poland and the then Soviet Union, the main scenes of the ultimate phase of the "Final Solution of the Jewish Question" – the extermination of European Jewry. True to say, part of the deportees did escape physical liquidation immediately after their arrival in those camps, as they were singled out to be gradually "worked to death" (Vernichtung durch Arbeit).

The first transports were dispatched from Terezín between January 9 and June 13, 1942. The first two transports traveled to the ghetto in Riga, the other to the so-called General Gouvernement, established in the central and south-eastern part of the Nazi-occupied Poland.

A more than 3-million strong Jewish community lived in Poland before World War II. After the country's occupation by Nazi Germany ghettos concentrating Jews were set up in many Polish towns. Later on, also the Jews deported from other European countries, including the then Protectorate of Bohemia and Moravia, were sent to the ghettos in Poland. The German occupation authorities proceeded in those territories much more brutally than in Central and Western Europe, and a substantial portion of the Jews in the East were decimated already in the local ghettos.

As a rule, the ghettos were set up in the most neglected parts of towns. Their inhabitants were crowded in a very small space, their accommodation and catering conditions being incredibly harrowing. They were mostly isolated from the outside world, separated either by fences or walls, and closely guarded. The remaining property and most of the things of daily use were confiscated from those prisoners immediately on arrival in the ghettos – of course provided these people had had any opportunity to take some luggage along before their summary eviction from their homes. Epidemics, absolute lack of medicaments, omnipresent famine and exhausting slave labor were the typical features characterizing an ordinary day in such a ghetto. Attempts

at establishing contacts with the outside world, getting extra food for themselves and the close relatives were punished by death. Old people and children, two age groups whose death-rates were terribly high, suffered most. For instance, some 80,000 people (one sixth of all the prisoners) in the Warsaw Ghetto died before the start of deportations to the extermination camps. Living in inhumane conditions, as many as 480,000 people were crammed in that ghetto. With most of its inmates deported to the Treblinka extermination camp during 1942, the Warsaw Ghetto was liquidated and razed to the ground, after the Nazis brutally suppressed the heroic uprising of the remaining Jews in April and May 1943. Up to 160,000 inmates languished in the Łódź Ghetto. Since that camp had some production capacities, it was liquidated gradually, mostly through a wave of deportations to the Kulmhof (Chełmno) extermination camp between January and May 1942. The final liquidation of the Łódź Ghetto came after deportations of its captive inhabitants to various concentration camps in early September 1944. Former Terezín Ghetto inmates were also interned in both of these largest ghettos as well as in the other ghettos and labor camps for the Jews in the East.

In the summer and fall of 1942 transports from Terezín were leaving for the Baltic region and Belorussia. The Jews from the German-dominated territories of the Soviet Union as well as other occupied European countries were killed there en masse. In actual fact, this genocide was in progress from the very beginning of Hitler's military campaign in the Soviet Union. Special SS task force units or death squads known as Einsatzgruppen, comprising members of the security police and security services, were deployed immediately behind the advancing frontline units. On the whole, there were four such formations, divided into a number of smaller squads known as Einsatzkommandos whose task was to comb the occupied territories and liquidate the "enemies of the Reich". In addition to the officials of the Soviet political and administrative authorities, the main enemies of the Reich were primarily the Jews.

According to incomplete German records,

these special task force groups killed at least 900,000 Jews, including thousands of prisoners who had arrived from the Terezín Ghetto. Most of them were sent to Maly Trostinec near Minsk. One of the Terezín transports, code-named AAy, was originally planned to reach that destination by the end of July 1942. Since dozens of thousands of Jews from the Minsk Ghetto were just being exterminated and – according to a written statement by one of the SS commanders "the personnel was overburdened" – the transport from Terezín was unloaded at the Baranowicze railway station, and its members murdered in a forest near the village of Kolpenice.

Still, the overall capacities of these SS death squads proved to be insufficient to meet the planned tasks of the "Final Solution". That was why extermination camps specializing in the most efficient methods of mass murder began to be built in the Polish territory. The first one was finished in the aforementioned town of Kulmhof by the end of 1941. In the following year, the mass killing of the Jews was concentrated in the extermination camps of Bełżec, Sobibór and Treblinka, where an operation code-named "Aktion Reinhard" (Action Reinhard) was in full swing. At the order of the SS Reichsführer Heinrich Himmler, stationary gas chambers killing people by exhaust fumes from tank engines were built in those camps. Some 1,750,000 people, mostly Polish Jews, were murdered in the gas chambers. Those victims comprised prisoners from other countries, including Terezín Ghetto inmates. Transports carrying predominantly elderly people from Terezín in September and October 1942 ended mostly at Treblinka, where they put about 18,000 people to death. In the summer of 1942, gas chambers were also put into operation in the Majdanek concentration and extermination camp, where also about 5,000 of Terezín inmates were killed.

(138) Jewish prisoners arriving in Riga for slave labor duty

(139) Members of a death squad (Einsatzkommando) who took part in killing prisoners in the ghettos

(140) Street in the Lublin Ghetto

(141) **Prisoners were either shot dead or killed in enclosed gas vans (pictured here)**

(142) **Mass execution of the Jews in Estonia. Dead bodies ready for burning**

(143) **Specially enclosed trucks or vans filled with gas were used for killing in the first extermination camp at Kulmhof. A transport carrying the victims arrives in the camp**

(144) **Rudolf Masárek, a former Terezín Ghetto prisoner, was one of the leaders of an uprising of the so-called Sonderkommando in Treblinka. He died in the uprising which helped part of the inmates to escape**

(145) **An aerial photo of the Sobibór extermination camp**

(146) **The railway station building at Treblinka where hundreds of thousands of Jews arrived to meet their death**

(147) The Auschwitz camp complex in an aerial picture taken by the US Air Force on June 26, 1944. Key:
I. Auschwitz I - Stammlager
II. Auschwitz II - Birkenau
III. Auschwitz III - Monowitz

The last of the transports dispatched from Terezín in 1942 left on October 26, reaching its new final destination – Auschwitz (Oświęcim). The largest complex of Nazi concentration camps was built around this town in Upper Silesia consisting of Auschwitz I - Stammlager (Core Camp), Auschwitz II - Birkenau (Brzezinka) and Auschwitz III - Monowitz (Monowice). Auschwitz II, where the Terezín transports arrived, remained deeply imprinted in the memory of all the survivors under its German name Birkenau. Auschwitz II was also an extermination camp and the Jews accounted for the largest number of its victims. Some 1,100,000 Jews were killed there. With the exception of two small transports to Bergen-Belsen all the other transports from Terezín headed to Birkenau.

Four crematoriums with gas chambers, using the deadly gas known as Zyklon B, were in operation in Birkenau. On arrival, during the so-called selections, the prisoners classified as fit for work were separated from "worthless eaters". Those branded as unfit to work by the SS doctors were sent to the gas chambers and killed. At least for a time those prisoners deemed fit for work retained their hopes for survival in the Nazi slave labor camps.

The industrial methods of killing reached their peak in Birkenau. The clothes, shoes, spectacles and other personal belongings of the victims were sorted out and sent to Germany for further use. Everything was utilized, even their mortal remains served as raw materials (manufacture of fabric from human hair etc.)

The fate of the Terezín Ghetto inmates sent in transports to Birkenau in September and December 1943 as well as May 1944 differed from that of the other transports to that destination. Their members were placed in the camp's sector BIIb, designated as the "Terezín family camp". Its establishment was motivated by the Nazi propaganda needs. Thousands of censored postcards sent by the inmates were intended to conceal the real fate awaiting the Jews "deployed for labor assignment" in the East as well as the truth about the Birkenau camp. Due to these reasons Reichsführer of the SS Himmler gave his permission in May 1944 for a foreign delegation to visit not only the Terezín Ghetto but also "one Jewish labor camp". There are signs that the "family camp" in Auschwitz was one of the sites singled out for this purpose.

On their arrival the prisoners placed in the "family camp" did not pass the usual selections. Family members were allowed mutual contact even though men, women and children were accommodated separately. On the other hand, these prisoners died there just as the inmates in the other sectors of the Birkenau camp – of hunger, exhaustion and contagious diseases. One in four prisoners who arrived from Terezín with the September 1943 transports died in the camp, while every third prisoner coming with the December transports perished in Auschwitz before the end of that year.

Those inmates in the "family camp", who survived the six-month long quarantine, were singled out for liquidation. 3,792 members of the September 1943 transports from Terezín were gassed to death in the gas chambers of the camp's crematoriums No. 2 and 3 during the night of March 8, 1944. These included some 3,700 Czech Jews. As a matter of record, this was the biggest mass murder of Czechoslovak citizens perpetrated during World War II.

The mass killing of the deportees who had come with the transports arriving in December 1943 planned for June 1944 was adjourned because of the Nazi fears of foreign protests. However, after a delegation of the International Committee of the Red Cross had visited Terezín, and its result proved to fit in with the Nazi propaganda goals, the very existence of the "family camp" in Auschwitz lost its meaning and the camp – together with the prisoners who had arrived only in May 1944 – was liquidated in July of that year. Some 3,500 men fit for work had been sent as slave laborers to various places, and some 6,500 remaining men, women and children were killed in the gas chambers between July 10 and 12, 1944.

(148) Selection in the camp Auschwitz II - Birkenau. All the people found unfit to work – children with their mothers, old and sick people – were sent to the left, their lives immediately ending in gas chambers. The able-bodied prisoners who were to be "worked to death" were sent to the right

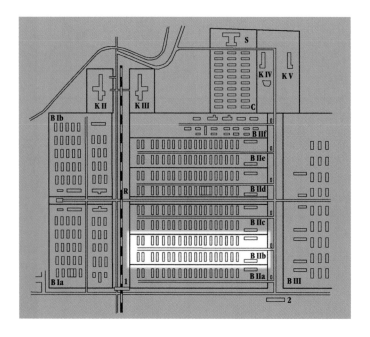

(149) Plan of sector BIIb of the Birkenau camp where the "Terezín family camp" was located

(150) One of the barracks in the "family camp"

(151) Building of crematorium No. 2 in Auschwitz

(152) Building of crematorium No. 3. 3,792 members of the transports from Terezín were gassed to death in the gas chambers of the camp's crematoriums No. 2 and 3 during the night of March 8, 1944

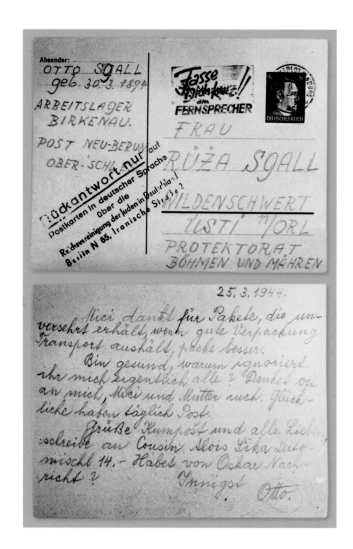

(153) Before leaving for their death in the gas chambers, the prisoners were forced to write postcards dated March 25, 1944. But by that time they had been dead for more than two weeks…

(154) After the departure of the prisoners who were found fit to work, the "family camp" was liquidated and its remaining inmates killed in July 1944. View from the arrival ramp towards the site of the "family camp"

The former prisoners of the Terezín Ghetto who survived the selections on their arrival in Auschwitz were sent for slave labor to many different places in Poland, Germany and Austria. In fact, the Nazi concentration camps provided a huge pool of forced labor for warring Germany. The former Terezín inmates capable of working were transferred primarily to the camp Auschwitz III, built by the Buna factory at Monowice, as well as to many of its subsidiary camps. Slave laborers from Terezín also toiled in other concentration camps – Sachsenhausen, Stutthof, Neuengamme, Mauthausen, Gross-Rosen, Bergen-Belsen, Flossenbürg, Buchenwald, Dachau – and their branches.

The process of mass killing in gas chambers in Auschwitz was terminated in November 1944. Soon afterwards the gas chambers and the crematoriums were blown up, and large numbers of the inmates were evacuated in truly inhumane conditions. On January 27, 1945, the Red Army liberated in Auschwitz as many as 7,000 remaining prisoners, including children used for pseudo-medical experiments.

The evacuation transports and death marches organized by the SS command in an attempt to move the inmates of the concentration camps before the advancing Allied armies eventually exacted the death of almost 250,000 people. Many former Terezín prisoners, who had left Auschwitz in such evacuation transports and death marches, died on their way. The final destination of some of those evacuation transports and death marches was Terezín. And indeed, more than 15,000 new prisoners arrived in the Ghetto at the very end of the war, including some 300 former Terezín prisoners who had been deported to Auschwitz earlier and who survived their slave labor ordeal in different parts of Europe.

All in all, almost 87,000 people were deported from Terezín to the East, an overwhelming majority of those people were killed or tortured to death. No more than some 3,600 of those who had been selected for slave labor and who survived the subsequent terrible hardships lived to see the end of the war.

(155) **The Golleschau (Goleszów) cement plant where an Auschwitz labor gang worked**

(156) **The factory producing synthetic gasoline at Blechhammer (Blachownia Śląska) also used Auschwitz prisoners as slave laborers. Part of the camp near the factory**

(157) **Bombed-out Hamburg. Former women prisoners from Terezín, deported from Auschwitz, cleared the rubble in the city**

(158) The Stutthof (Sztutowo) concentration camp and its subsidiary camps where several hundred women prisoners from the "Terezín family camp" in Auschwitz worked as slave laborers

(159) A large group of Terezín prisoners who arrived from Auschwitz to Kaufering in Bavaria on October 25, 1944, worked on the construction of underground aircraft factories. Part of the list of prisoners of Kaufering

(160) Subsidiary camp of the Mauthausen concentration camp at Gusen. Former Terezín inmates used to work in its underground facilities

(161) The arrival in Bergen-Belsen of a large group of exhausted, starving and ill prisoners from the other evacuated camps resulted in a sharp increase in its death-rate. The victims included many former Terezín inmates. Burial into a mass grave after the camp's liberation

(162) Beginning on January 18, 1945, the prisoners from Auschwitz were evacuated before the approaching Allied forces. An evacuation transport passing through Velim railway station

(163) **The ruins of a destroyed gas chamber in crematorium No. 2 in Auschwitz**

(164) **Exhumation of a mass grave containing the bodies of the victims of a death march from Schwarzheide to Terezín**

(165) **The lobby of the Museum houses short-term exhibitions**

(166) **Scale model of the Terezín Ghetto in the lobby of the Museum**

(167) **The Museum's cinema hall**

(168) **The study room in the Museum**

OTHER PREMISES OF THE GHETTO MUSEUM

The Terezín Memorial uses for its activities other premises of the Ghetto Museum as well. The foyer of the cinema is the site of short-term exhibitions, also featuring an electronically controlled scale model of the Ghetto. Made after an original plaster mock-up fashioned by the Terezín inmates in 1944, it is used to show groups of visitors what the Ghetto really looked like during World War II. Handbooks in four languages available on a rack near the model advise visitors how to handle the model, also providing a wealth of detailed information on the individual objects in the Ghetto. Visitors may also like to watch different documentaries screened in the cinema. The first (ground) floor of the building houses a study room which also serves as a lecture hall.

TEREZÍN MEMORIAL

Established in 1947, the Terezín Memorial was originally known as the Memorial of National Suffering. Its main mission is to commemorate the victims and the suffering of prisoners of the former Terezín Ghetto, the Gestapo Police Prison in the Small Fortress and the concentration camp in the nearby town of Litoměřice. Today the Terezín Memorial is a museum, research and educational institution administering a complex of objects and memorial sites that commemorate the most tragic chapter in modern European history. The Terezín Memorial is the only institution of its kind in the Czech Republic.

In actual fact, all the objects and memorial sites administered by the Terezín Memorial are annually visited by hundreds of thousands of people from all over the world. Some of them also come to admire the highlights of 18th century European fortification engineering which can be viewed in Terezín's extensive fortifications. But an overwhelming majority of visitors arrive to see the sites connected with the suffering and death of dozens of thousands of innocent people who fell victims of the Nazi reign of terror.

The history of the former Terezín Ghetto is today traced and highlighted in the exhibitions housed in the Ghetto Museum, in the crematorium in the Jewish Cemetery, in the former Central Mortuary and the Ghetto's Columbarium as well as in the former Magdeburg Barracks. There are other objects and memorial sites in and around Terezín associated with the history of the Terezín Ghetto.

Situated not far from the town is the Small Fortress which housed the Prague Gestapo Police Prison during World War II. Visitors may like to see its compound with former prison cells and other objects as well as the Small Fortress Museum offering two permanent exhibitions and other permanent as well as short-term exhibitions on display in the Small Fortress.

Spreading in the foreground of the Small Fortress is the National Cemetery where some of the victims of the three above-mentioned repressive facilities in Terezín and Litoměřice are buried. This is also the site of the annual Terezín Commemoration, the Czech Republic's central act of remembrance to honor the memory of the victims of Nazi occupation during the war.

The Terezín Memorial also administers the crematorium of the Litoměřice concentration camp and the entrance object to the nearby underground factory built by the inmates of the concentration camp who had to work under incredibly hard conditions, and later also to work in the production of this factory. The underground premises are today closed to visitors because of the permanent danger of landslides.

In addition to guided sightseeing tours of the former Ghetto and the Gestapo Police Prison in the Small Fortress, coming complete with expert explanation, also the crematorium of the former Litoměřice concentration camp can be visited after prior booking.

Apart from the permanent exhibitions, throughout the year visitors can also view short-term documentary and fine art displays in the exhibition halls in the Small Fortress and the Ghetto Museum.

Researchers and scholars can study the funds of the Memorial's Departments of Documentation and Collections and use its specialized library.

The staff of the Terezín Memorial also provide consultations on matters of racial and political persecution in World War II as well as information on the fate of individual prisoners in the repressive facilities in Terezín and Litoměřice.

PAMÁTNÍK TEREZÍN

MALÁ PEVNOST — MUZEUM GHETTA

TEREZÍN MEMORIAL

PERMANENT EXHIBITIONS OF THE TEREZÍN MEMORIAL:

- The Terezín Small Fortress 1940–1945 – an exhibition in the Small Fortress Museum

- Art exhibition of the Terezín Memorial – an exhibition in the Small Fortress Museum

- Litoměřice Concentration Camp 1944–1945 – an exhibition in the Third Courtyard of the Small Fortress

- Terezín 1780–1939 – an exhibition in the entrance to the Small Fortress

- The Detention Camp for the Germans. The Small Fortress 1945–1948 – an exhibition in the Fourth Courtyard of the Small Fortress

- Terezín in the "Final Solution of the Jewish Question" 1941–1945 – an exhibition in the Ghetto Museum

- Mortality and Burials in the Terezín Ghetto – an exhibition in the crematorium at the Jewish Cemetery

- Central Mortuary and Funeral Services in the Ghetto – an exhibition in the Ghetto's former Central Mortuary

- A reconstruction of prisoners' dormitory at the time of the Ghetto – an exhibition in the former Magdeburg Barracks

- Music in the Terezín Ghetto – an exhibition in the former Magdeburg Barracks

- Art in the Terezín Ghetto – an exhibition in the former Magdeburg Barracks

- Literary Work in the Terezín Ghetto – an exhibition in the former Magdeburg Barracks

- Theater in the Terezín Ghetto – an exhibition in the former Magdeburg Barracks

OBJECTS OF THE TEREZÍN MEMORIAL AND MEMORIAL SITES FROM THE YEARS 1940–1945

1 The Ghetto Museum. *Terezín's former municipal school housed a boys' home at the time of the Ghetto. The building is now the site of a permanent exhibition on the history of the Terezín Ghetto, housing a cinema, premises for occasional exhibitions, a reading room and offices of the Memorial's Department of Education where visitors may also get specialized information.*

2 The Small Fortress. *Visitors may view this former Gestapo Police Prison. There are permanent exhibitions, short-term displays and a cinema in the Small Fortress Museum as well in other parts of the compound. Specialized information will be provided to visitors by guides or by the staff of the Departments of History and Documentation.*

3 The National Cemetery. *Founded in 1945, it contains graves of the victims from the Gestapo Police Prison in the Small Fortress, the Terezín Ghetto and the concentration camp in Litoměřice.*

4 Memorial site near the Ohře. *The ashes of some 22,000 victims, cremated in the Ghetto crematorium, were thrown into the river on this site at the order of the SS Camp headquarters in November 1944.*

5 The Terezín Children's Park. *It was built in commemoration of the youngest victims of the Ghetto as a place of remembrance.*

6 The former Magdeburg Barracks. *At the time of the Ghetto the seat of the Jewish Self-Administration, the object now houses the Terezín Memorial's Meeting Center where various educational programs are held, a reconstructed prisoners' dormitory from the time of the Ghetto, and permanent exhibitions tracing different walks of cultural life in the Ghetto.*

7 Jewish Prayer Room. *A unique room for religious ceremonies, built by the prisoners, with partly preserved original decorations, has survived in an outhouse in one of the Terezín yards.*

8 The railway siding. *The remnants of the railway line on the former track connecting the Terezín Ghetto with the railway station at Bohušovice nad Ohří.*

9 The Columbarium. *The ashes of the Ghetto victims cremated in the local crematorium are kept in this part of the former fortifications. Today it houses reconstructed equipment from the time of the Ghetto and a room containing memorial plaques.*

10 The Ceremonial Halls *and* The Central Mortuary of the Ghetto. *Dead bodies were kept and mass funerals and prayers were held in these premises. These have been adequately reconstructed, and the Central Mortuary now houses an exhibition on these premises and on burial services in the Ghetto as well as samples of soil from the places where most Terezín Ghetto inmates perished after their deportation to the East.*

11 The Jewish Cemetery *and* The crematorium. *Permanent exhibition devoted to mortality and burials in the Ghetto may be viewed in the crematorium.*

12 The Soviet Military Cemetery. *Citizens of the former Soviet Union who were killed in and around Terezín at the end of the war or who died when fighting a spotted fever epidemic in the Ghetto during the first weeks after its liberation are buried in the cemetery.*

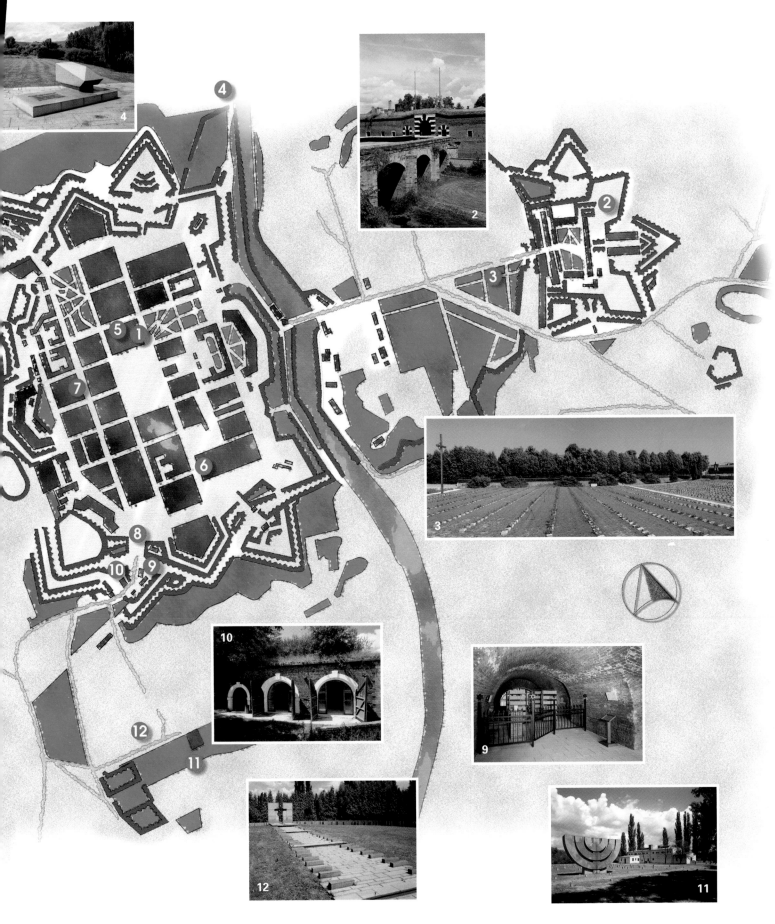

PLAN OF THE FORMER GHETTO MARKING STOPS ON A GUIDED TOUR

1 L 417, Hauptstrasse 17
(The designation of the individual buildings in the Ghetto using the initial letters L – Langstrasse {longitudinal street} and Q – Querstrasse {cross-street} ended at the time of what was called the "beautification" of Terezín. Its streets received "civilian" names better corresponding with the SS propaganda aims. The names of the barracks in the Ghetto were taken over from the German Army which renamed the objects after Nazi occupation of the Czech lands in March 1939.)
Today's Ghetto Museum. Formerly Terezín's municipal school began to serve in 1942 for the accommodation of boys aged 10–15 who lived in the so-called heims (homes). Clandestine classes were held mostly in its attic premises, the gym – today cinema hall – was the venue of many performances of musical and dramatic works (e. g. performance of Smetana's opera Prodaná nevěsta (The Bartered Bride). The boys living in home No. 1 established their own self-administration called "ŠKID Republic" and for two years published their magazine "Vedem". Lectures, cultural programs and debates with famous scientists and artists were also held in the building. This was an unofficial hub of the cultural life of the Ghetto's young people.

2 Q 619, Rathausgasse 19
The Terezín Town Hall served in the Ghetto as the seat of several "institutions". Among other offices this was the seat of the Ghetto Court and – since May 1943 – it housed the offices of the Bank of the Jewish Self-Administration. Its main hall, used as a concert hall, also housed a library for a time. Part of the attic premises were turned into wooden attic flats. After the country's liberation in 1945 it was the seat of the Soviet headquarters, today housing the Municipal Council.

3 L 414, Hauptstrasse 14
Originally the seat of the Fortress Headquarters. Until August 1942 the seat of the SS Camp headquarters, later its first (ground) floor premises housed a post-office where parcels sent to the Ghetto inmates were inspected and distributed. The upper floors housed a dormitory primarily for youth coming in German transports. Girls from the Protectorate, who issued their own magazine "Bonaco", were also accommodated there.

4 L 410, Hauptstrasse 10
This building served as a dormitory for girls aged 8–16 years. Clandestine school lessons were given in the building, also attended by older girls after their return from work. The SS headquarters permitted drawing lessons, led by Friedl Dicker-Brandeisová, to be given in the building. Verdi's Requiem, Smetana's opera Prodaná nevěsta (The Bartered Bride) and other works were rehearsed in its cellars.

5 Marktplatz
In 1943 a larger part of the square was taken up by a three-part big tent, serving as the workshop for the so-called "K-production" (Kistenproduktion) where prisoners assembled covers for devices designed for defreezing car and truck engines at the eastern front. Almost the entire perimeter of the square was fenced off and access was allowed through guarded entrances with barriers. As part of the town's "beautification" campaign, early in 1944 the square was turned into a park with flowerbeds and benches. A wooden music pavilion for promenade concerts was erected in the square.

6 L 415, Hauptstrasse 15
A store selling clothes and underwear was opened in the first (ground) floor of the building. Most of the goods on sale came from the luggage of the prisoners confiscated on their arrival. Several other similar "stores", set up as part of the SS propaganda campaign, were also situated in the streets L 3 and L 4 (Lange Strasse and Hauptstrasse).

7 Q 418, Neue Gasse 18
A café offering seats for some 100 people was opened in the first (ground) floor of the building on December 6, 1942. The café was opened from 10 a. m. to 7:30 p. m. The prisoners who obtained tickets could sit there for 90 minutes drinking a cup of ersatz coffee, listening to music or watching cabaret scenes.

8 Q 414,416. Neue Gasse 14 a 16
Beginning in August 1942, this building housed the SS Camp headquarters (SS-Lagerkommandantur Theresienstadt). Its cellars contained the so-called bunkers where offenders who had violated the camp's regulations were jailed, tortured and interrogated by the Gestapo. Today this building houses a branch of Česká spořitelna (Czech Savings Bank).

9 L 311, Lange Strasse 11
The Engineering Barracks. At the time of the Ghetto this housed the home for the aged and a makeshift hospital for old prisoners with urological and neurological outpatient clinics, an outpatient clinic for lung diseases and the treatment or tuberculosis and a ward for cardiac

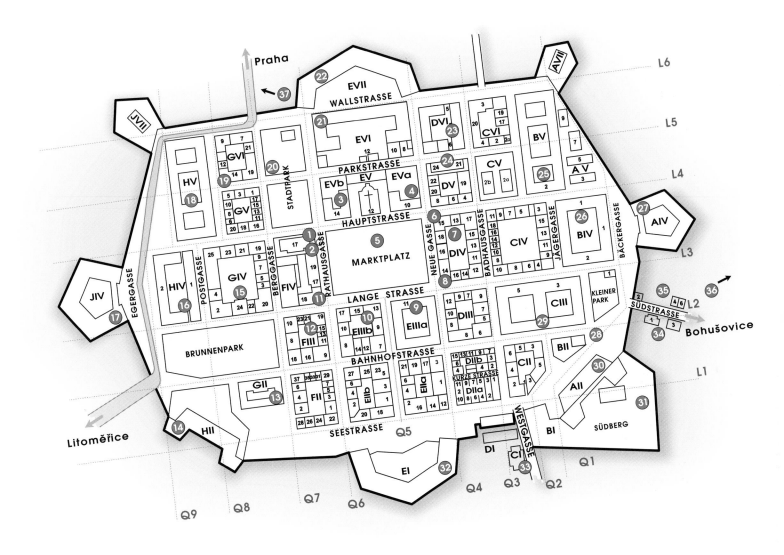

diseases. There was a kitchen in the object as well. Some of the premises were used for cultural purposes and lectures, a prayer room was established in its attic, alternately serving believers of different religions. Today it houses the Social Welfare Institute of the capital city of Prague.

10 L 315, Lange Strasse 15
This was the seat of the Ghetto Guards (Ghettowache), charged to supervise internal law and order in the Ghetto. The only weapons carried by the guards were wooden truncheons. And yet, after the anti-Nazi uprising in the Warsaw Ghetto, this unit, mostly consisting of younger men with military training, was disbanded at the orders of the SS Camp headquarters – evidently because of fears that its members might form a resistance group. Almost all of its members were deported to be killed in Auschwitz. Later restored, the guard unit consisted of older men aged 45 who were not allowed to live in the same building. The object houses a hall used until 1943 for cultural programs. Today's Community Center.

11 L 318, Lange Strasse 18
This used to house the home for children of preschool and early school age. The smallest kids would return to their mothers for the night. The building also housed a kitchen for children with a dining room and a bakery. Meals were sent to other homes, some of the children would eat in the local dining room. Stage plays for children were performed in one of its halls. Today's Post-Office building.

12 Block F III
This block of flats housed many homes for children and youth, a sickbay, an outpatient clinic for youth as well as a theater hall. A library for youth was located in L 216 (Bahnhofstrasse 16).

13 Block G II

The former officers' casino used to house the dormitory of a special unit of the Protectorate gendarmerie which guarded the barracks housing deported Jews in the early days of the Ghetto. Beginning in the middle of 1942, when the whole town was turned into the Ghetto, the gendarmes were sent on guard duty at the borders of the Ghetto and escorts of the inmates outside the Ghetto.

14 Block H II

The workshop yard called Bauhof. This concentrated various Ghetto workshops which produced, for instance, sectional wooden barracks to be assembled on the building site. A gas chamber had been built in the corridor of the fortress ravelin XVIII at the end of the war but was not finished.

15 L 324, Lange Strasse 24

This hotel building served as dormitory for the SS staff (SS-Kameradschaftsheim), later called Viktoria-Haus. There was a dining hall on its first (ground) floor, with dormitories on the upper floors. The Ghetto prisoners were strictly forbidden to enter the object. Today Parkhotel.

16 Block H IV

The Bodenbach Barracks were first used as accommodation facilities, then – for a time – as a "šlojska". This slang expression used in the Ghetto was derived from the German word "die Schleusse" (sluice) and denoted a checkpoint where people arriving in transports were checked together with their luggage. Prisoners would then leave for their assigned dormitories. During deportations to the East, prisoners leaving for transports were assembled there. Many different objects in Terezín served as "šlojska" (checkpoint). The Bodenbach Barracks, together with some other objects, had to be quickly vacated on July 1943 and handed over for the needs of the archives of the Reich Security Main Office.

17 Block J IV

The Aussig Barracks also served for a time as a "šlojska" (checkpoint) but it primarily housed the central food warehouse, later central clothing warehouse. All the luggage of the incoming transports began to be brought into the building in July 1942. Clothes were sorted out, better pieces were dispatched to Germany, lower-quality clothing was sent to Terezín's "stores" for prisoners. Two mass executions, during which 16 prisoners were hanged for paltry offenses, were held by the walls near these barracks on January 10 and February 26, 1942.

18 Block H V

The Dresden Barracks. Accommodated in this object were women, initially with their children. There were prison cells for offenders among the inmates on the first (ground) floor. An outpatient clinic and a sickroom were situated in other parts of the complex. Some of the premises were used as lecture and theater halls.

A makeshift soccer pitch was built in the yard of the barracks but due to lack of space each team could have only seven players. The famous scenes of a soccer match for the Nazi propaganda documentary film were shot in this yard.

19 Block G VI

Mothers with children up to 3 years of age were accommodated in several houses there. A concert and theater hall was built in the former cinema in L 514 (Parkstrasse 14). At the end of 1943, this building housed a library containing several thousand volumes and a reading room for more than 100 people. The whole block burnt out at the end of the war.

20 Stadtpark

The relatively well-kept municipal park was inaccessible to the inmates for a long time. A wooden children's pavilion, a playground, a paddling pool, swings and other equipment were built there during the "beautification" campaign in Terezín. But the local children could use these facilities only immediately before and during the visit to Terezín paid by a delegation of the International Committee of the Red Cross.

21 Block E VI

The Hohenelbe Barracks. Originally the garrison hospital, which served during the time of the Ghetto as its Central Hospital with a central laboratory. This object also housed the central baths with a small swimming pool and a kitchen catering for the infirm.

22 Block E VII

The Kavalír Barracks, known in the Ghetto slang as "Kavalírka". A "šlojska" (checkpoint) was based there for several months in 1942, later this object was infamous as a home for elderly inmates. Mentally ill patients, separated from the rest of the inmates by a high wooden fence, lived in one wing of the object.

23 Block D VI

The former brewery housed partly a women's dormitory but it was largely used as a disinfecting station, baths and laundry.

24 Q 321 a Q 424 (Badhausgasse 21 a Neue Gasse 24)

The former riding hall served as a "šlojska" (checkpoint). A mechanical joiner's workshop manufacturing mostly furniture was established in the object in 1943.

25 Block B V

The Magdeburg Barracks, the seat of the Elder of the Jews, the Council of Elders and the Jewish Self-Administration's office. The leading officials of the Self-Administration also had their modest flats there, mostly a single room for the whole family. Some of the premises were used for cultural programs and meetings of the inmates.

26 Block B IV

The Hannover Barracks housed a dormitory for men fit to work. One of the large-capacity kitchens was also there. The cellars were used for rehearsals of different musical performances.

27 Block A IV
This former army bakery also served at the time of the Ghetto as its central bakery and food warehouse.

28 Bahnhofstrasse
Part of this street was taken up by a railway siding built by the inmates between 1942 and 1943. It led from the Bohušovice nad Ohří railway station, some 3 kilometers distant, up to house L 227 (Bahnhofstrasse 27). The first train arrived there on June 1, 1943. From then on, all the transports arrived into and left the Ghetto without the prisoners coming into any contact with people living in the vicinity. A "šlojska" (checkpoint) was built in the Hamburg Barracks at the end of the railway siding, and all the incoming and outgoing transports had to pass through this checkpoint.

29 Block C III
The Hamburg Barracks originally served as a women's dormitory, later as a dormitory for Jews from the Netherlands, and a "šlojska". Cabaret performances were held in the first-floor warehouse (e. g. by Kurt Gerron).

30 Block A II
The Jäger Barracks located in the casemates near the former Bohušovice Gate. It served as a "šlojska" (checkpoint), quarantine area and a dormitory for the aged.

31 Südberg
The Southern Hill on the site of the former bastion III of the old fortifications. Originally, the Ghetto inmates had no access to this area. A sports ground for children and adults was set up there in 1943 as part of the Nazi campaign to paint a distorted picture of ordinary life in what they called "Jewish settlement territory". Pitches for soccer, basketball and volleyball courts were also built.

32 Block E I
The Sudeten Barracks. The first transport bringing 342 young men arrived in this object on November 24, 1941. Whole families came in the following transports. Two weeks later women with children were transferred to the Dresden Barracks. One of the camp's large-capacity kitchens was in operation in the object. As many as 6,000 prisoners were accommodated in the barracks. All the inmates had to move out of the building in a matter of several days in July 1943 and until the end of the war this and some other buildings housed part of the Reich Security Main Office archives from Berlin. As a result, the Ghetto inmates served as "live shields" protecting the important Reich Security Main Office documents against Allied air raids. A quarantine hospital for the prisoners from the Small Fortress suffering from spotted fever was set up in the object in May 1945.

33 Objekt C I
Former Sokol gym first served for the accommodation of children suffering from encephalitis. Also sick children from the Białystok Ghetto were kept in isolation in the building. During the "beautification" campaign it was turned into the so-called Community Center offering two halls for music and theater performances, a library, a prayer room and a relaxation area on the terrace.

34 Südstrasse
The Central Mortuary was established in one sector of the former fortification in August 1942. Dead bodies were brought to the Mortuary immediately after being examined by a physician. Whenever possible, funeral (later cremation) was held on the following day. Ceremonial Halls were set up next to the Mortuary, where the mourners could pay their last respects. These were mass funeral services for several dozens of victims. One of the halls was used for the deceased of the Jewish belief, the other for Christians. As a matter of fact, many Christians were classified as Jews under the infamous Nuremberg Laws and as such they were subjected to the Nazi criminal program known as the "Final Solution of the Jewish Question".

35 Südstrasse
The Columbarium is situated in the former fortification on the opposite side of the road. Between 1942 and 1944, the ashes of the victims cremated in the crematorium in the Jewish Cemetery were put into paper funeral urns and stored in the Columbarium. At the order of the SS headquarters part of the ashes was buried near the Litoměřice concentration camp and a larger part was thrown into the river Ohře in November 1944.

36 Bauschowitzer Kessel
The Jewish Cemetery and crematorium. As many as 9,000 bodies were buried in individual and primarily mass graves in the Cemetery during the first year of the Ghetto's existence and later at the end of the war. Initially, the dead were buried in individual graves but soon only into mass graves. The growing mortality rate in the Ghetto called for the construction of a crematorium which started its operation in September 1942. Up to the end of the war some 30,000 bodies, including those of the victims from the Gestapo Police Prison in the Small Fortress and the concentration camp in Litoměřice, were cremated there.

37 Memorial Site by the Ohře river
In November 1944, the ashes of 22,000 victims cremated in the crematorium in the Jewish Cemetery were thrown into the Ohře river on the site of a former berth for fishermen's boats.

LIST OF REPRODUCED EXHIBITS

The list of reproduced exhibits selected for this book on the Ghetto Museum is numbered in the same way as the list in the book. This list gives additional data on the exhibits (such as technique used, dimensions, collection, inventory number). The actual position of any signs or signatures in the drawings is described by abbreviations BR / BL: bottom right / bottom left etc. Dimensions are given in millimeters, starting with height and followed by width. Italic is used to designate the titles of stage plays, operas, books etc. as used in the Terezín Ghetto.

Key to Abbreviations:

BR	bottom right	SÚA	State Central Archives in Prague
TR	top right	APMO	Archiwum Państwowego Muzeum Auschwitz-Birkenau w Oświęcimiu, Oświęcim, Poland
BL	bottom left		
CL	center left	BPK	Bildarchiv Preussischer Kulturbesitz, Berlin, Germany
TL	top left		
PT	Terezín Memorial's Collections	CICR	Comité international de la Croix-Rouge, Genève, Switzerland
APT	Terezín Memorial's Archive		
FAPT	Terezín Memorial's Photo-Archive	NIOD	Nederlands Instituut voor Oorlogsdocumentatie, Amsterdam, Netherlands
JMP	Jewish Museum in Prague		
ČTK	Czech Press Agency in Prague	YV FA	Yad Vashem Film&Photo Archive, Jerusalem, Israel
NFA	National Film Archives in Prague		

(1) Entrance to the Ghetto Museum
Photo: M. Posselt

(2) The first exhibition hall on the Museum's ground (first) floor
Photo: M. Posselt

(3) Fortress Terezín on a wall drawing by M. Ressel on display in the first exhibition hall
Photo: M. Posselt

(4) An object made up of the original transport suitcases in the first hall of the exhibition on the first (ground) floor of the Ghetto Museum
Photo: M. Posselt

(5) The walls of the Memorial Hall commemorating the youngest victims of the Terezín Ghetto are covered with the names of 8,000 children
Photo: M. Posselt

(6) Photograph of sister and brother L. and J. Pollak
JMP, Sb. fot., I 21a/15, č. neg. 33205

(7) Photograph of Z. Koňas
JMP, Sb. fot., I 21 a/3, neg. č. 24157

(8) Photograph of M. Castelinová
JMP, Sb. fot., I 21 a/9, č. neg. 33877

(9) Photograph of the children in the Terezín Ghetto taken during a visit by a delegation of the International Committee of the Red Cross
CICR – neg. HIST 1160/11

(10) Photograph of the children in the Terezín Ghetto taken during a visit by a delegation of the International Committee of the Red Cross
CICR – neg. HIST 1162/2

(11) F. Bass's poem Zahrada taken from: Dětské kresby na zastávce k smrti. Terezín 1942–1944, Státní židovské museum Praha 1959, p. 50

(12) Cover page of the magazine "Vedem" Magazine "Vedem" No. 9 from February 12, 1943, p. 51, APT A 1317

(13) Drawing of H. Fischl
BL: Fischl, BR: II. / Gruppe / Hons
pastel drawing, paper, 203 x 296, JMP 125523, © Jewish Museum in Prague

(14) Drawing of L. Franklová
TL: Liana Franklová
pencil and pastel wash drawing, paper, 216 x 342, JMP 129378, © Jewish Museum in Prague

(15) Drawing of J. Agularová
pencil and pastel drawing, paper, 203 x 288, JMP 125732, © Jewish Museum in Prague

(16) Drawing of R. Heinová
BR: Rut Hein
pastel wash drawing, paper, 163 x 203, JMP 129364, © Jewish Museum in Prague

(17) Collage from the drawings made by the children in the Terezín Ghetto, placed in the Museum's staircase
Photo: M. Posselt

(18) H. Weissová: Children going to school, 1942
BR: Helga Weiss 12 Jahre / Dresdner Kaserne hw
pen drawing, watercolor, paper, 165 x 197, H. Hošková's collection

(19) H. Weissová: Arrival in Terezín, 1942
BR: Helga Weiss / 520/L Dresdner / 217
pen drawing, watercolor, paper, 150 x 220, H. Hošková's collection

(20) Poster column covered with anti-Jewish notices and regulations from the time of the Nazi occupation
Photo: M. Posselt

(21) Cover page of a special issue No.11 of the magazine "Der Stürmer" from November 1938
JMP, DP, i. č. 88a

(22) Cover of a German schoolbook entitled "Der Giftpilz"
JMP, knihovna, VIII-86, "Der Giftpilz"

(23) Chart for the identification of Jews according to the Nuremberg Laws
JMP, Sb. fot., I/3, č. neg. 21245

(24) Photograph of a burning synagogue in Baden-Baden
ČTK 32 567/2

(25) Photograph depicting the arrival of the Nazi occupation forces in Prague on March 15, 1939
ČTK 51626/35

(26) Map of the Protectorate marking its Oberlandrats (districts)
taken from: Židé v protektorátu. Hlášení židovské náboženské obce v roce 1942. Dokumenty, vyd. Helena Krejčová, Jana Svobodová, Anna Hyndráková, Ústav pro soudobé dějiny AV ČR, Praha 1997, p. 56

(27) Photograph of H. Bonn
JMP, Sb. fot., I/44, č. neg. 5214

(28) Photo showing the registration of the Jews
JMP, Sb. fot. I/14/b, č. neg. 21767

(29) Photograph of a classroom in a Jewish school
JMP, Sb. fot. I/20 a, č. neg. 24908

(30) L. Haas: Nisko camp, February 6, 1940
BR: LEO / HAAS / BARACKENLAGER NISKO / am / BARÁKOVÝ TÁBOR na / SAN. / ZARZECZE, 6. II.1940 / Leo Haas collotype, ozalid, paper pasted on cardboard, 190 x 395, PT 1527

(31) View of the first exhibition room on the second floor
Photo: M. Posselt

(32) View of the main exhibition room on the second floor
Photo: M. Posselt

(33) Excerpt from the minutes from a meeting of Heydrich's staff on October 10, 1941
APT A 331/81

(34) Excerpt from the minutes from a meeting of Heydrich's staff on October 17, 1941
APT MF 355

(35) Photograph of a sealed Jewish flat
JMP, Sb. fot. I/27, č. neg. 5508

(36) Photograph of confiscated Jewish furniture stored in a synanogue
JMP, Sb. fot. I/7, č. neg. 5093

(37) Photograph of a transport on its way from the Bohušovice nad Ohří railway station to Terezín
JMP, Sb. fot., II/1, č. neg. 24762

(38) L. Haas: Members of the SS Camp headquarters
pencil drawing, paper, 175 x 126, PT 1887

(39) Photograph of the gallows at the Aussig Barracks
FAPT A 4416

(40) Photograph of the bunkers beneath the SS Camp headquarters
FAPT 3666

(41) Photograph of the roll-call of a special unit of the Protectorate gendarmerie
JMP, Sb. fot., II/46-1, č. neg. 29547

(42) Photograph of a group of guards in the Gestapo Police Prison in the Small Fortress
FAPT A 880

(43) Entrance to the so-called Jewish cells in the Small Fortress
FAPT 6051/5, Photo: J. Nováková

(44) The first order of the day issued by the Jewish Self-Administration of the Terezín Ghetto on December 15, 1941
NIOD, 250/A, Doss. 5, Mape 9A

(45) Photograph of J. Edelstein
JMP, Sb. fot., II/41-1, č. neg. 51444

(46) Photograph from a meeting of the Council of Elders of the Terezín Ghetto
NFA – FAPT A 806

(47) Figurines of a girl and a boy leaving for a transport
PT 7285, Photo: M. Posselt

(48) A commemorative sheet marking the last day of the Protectorate postal service in Terezín
APT A 26/1

(49) A report from the Gestapo office at Würzburg on preparations for transports to be sent to Terezín
NIOD, 250 N/4, 6 A, 116

(50) Order of the day of the Jewish Self-Administration No. 20 from January 5, 1942
JMP, T, i. č. 173

(51) Announcement of the Jewish Self-Administration from October 1942 on transports of elderly prisoners
APT A 1842

(52) Photograph of a train in the railway siding in Terezín taken on June 1, 1943
JMP, Sb. fot. II/31, č. neg. 20854

(53) L. Haas: Roll-call in the Bohušovice Basin
BR: Lev Haas
etching, paper, 374 x 500, PT 1935

(54) Announcement of the Jewish Self-Administration No. 16
APT A 3471

(55) Last-minute preparations for the visit to Terezín by a delegation of the International Committee of the Red Cross in a drawing by Alfred Kantor
taken from: Das Buch von Alfred Kantor, Frankfurt/M. 1989, Fig. 18

(56) Banknotes used in the Terezín Ghetto
APT A 8890, K 44/gh.

(57) Audiences in a lecture room in a shot from a Nazi propaganda documentary
NFA – FAPT A 1962

(58) Call-up paper for the "Swiss" transport
APT A 41/4-1

(59) Photograph of the space in front of the unfinished gas chamber
FAPT A 1903

(60) Charred document from the former RSHA archive
APT A 7195

(61) Photograph of a wagon with prisoners in an evacuation transport
FAPT A 398

(62) Photograph of the arrival of the Red Army troops in Terezín
FAPT A 384

(63) Photograph of a notice board warning against spotted fever epidemics
FAPT A 385

(64) Photograph of orphaned Jewish children in a convalescent home at Kamenice near Popovice
FAPT 4511/3

(65) Photograph of a train with former prisoners on the Terezín railway siding before departure
JMP, Sb. fot., II/25, č. neg. 20872

(66) Photograph of K. Rahm, the last Terezín camp commander, before execution
FAPT A 1064

(67) Photograph of K. Körper
FAPT 793

(68) A clandestinely made radio set built into a suitcase
JMP, sb. př. 104954, Photo: M. Posselt

(69) Photograph of a woman prisoner sitting in a bunk
JMP, Sb. fot. II/31, č. neg. 20877

(70) F. M. Nágl: Prison sleeping quarters
BR: NÁGL.
combined technique, carton, 220 x 299, PT 6278

(71) F. Bloch: Sleeping quarters in the loft
BR: feb
charcoal and French chalk drawing, paper, 403 x 286, JMP 176335, © Jewish Museum in Prague

(72) Photograph of men's sleeping quarters in the Hannover Barracks
FAPT A 788

(73) J. T. Spitz: A crowd waiting for food
BR: příteli Honzovi / Tomy Spitz.
pencil drawing, paper, 222 x 150, PT 8581

(74) J. Schubert: Scraping scraps of food from casks, 1943
BR: Schubert 43
India ink wash drawing, carton, 218 x 277, PT 8286

(75) L. Haas: An old woman waiting for food, 1943
BL: Leo Haas 43
pencil drawing, cardboard, 275 x 203, PT 1693

(76) A special voucher for waste vegetables
APT A 82/26

(77) Food coupons for the prisoners
APT A 11832, A 11833, A 11834, A 11836

(78) K. Fleischmann: Sick women in the attic of L 504, 1943
BL: L 504, BR: KF 43
pencil drawing, paper, 209 x 273, JMP 175320, © Jewish Museum in Prague

(79) F. Bloch: A burial service
BL: feb
India ink drawing, paper, 227 x 345, JMP 173976, © Jewish Museum in Prague

(80) A tag tied to the leg of dead bodies in the Ghetto
APT A 82/14

(81) K. Fleischmann: Paying last respects in the mortuary, 1943
BR: KF 43
pencil drawing, paper, 208 x 147, JMP 175252, © Jewish Museum in Prague

(82) A table with charts showing the number of suicides, suicide attempts as well as the actual suicide methods used up to the end of 1943
APT A 1331/5

(83) K. Fleischmann: Loading coffins on a flatbed, 1943
TR: TEREZÍN – 1943. / K. FLEISCHMANN.
BR: KF 43
pen and India ink wash drawing, watercolor, carton, 520 x 1508, PT 13148

(84) B. Fritta: Army uniform repair shop
collotype, ozalid, paper, 175 x 120, PT 5024/2

(85) Photograph of prisoner D. Schimmerlingová grazing sheep
FAPT A 4424

(86) Photograph of the construction of barracks housing a mica-splitting operation and export production facilities
FAPT A 790

(87) An anonymous author: Drawing of the Wulkow camp
photograph, APT A 2939

(88) Photograph of the chateau at Panenské Břežany
FAPT 5184

(89) L. Kollinský's work card
APT A 3190

(90) O. Ungar: Building the railway siding, 1943
BR: Ungar / 1943
pencil drawing, carton, 247 x 347, PT 8185

(91) Photograph of physician E. Munk
JMP, Sb. fot. II/41-5, č. neg. 40919

(92) N. Troller: Surgery in the Ghetto, 1943
BL: Terezín 43, BR: Trollerarch
pencil drawing, paper, 280 x 264, PT 7364

(93) K. Fleischmann:: Dormitory for blind women, 1943
BL: K. Fleischmann / TEREZÍN – 1943
India ink drawing, carton, 695 x 625, PT 13147

(94) Figurine of a nurse
PT 7287, Photo: M. Posselt

(95) L. Haas: In the Terezín hospital, August 4, 1943
BR: 4. VIII.1943
India ink drawing, paper, 382 x 500, JMP 173559

(96) A table describing the Ghetto's health-care system as an illustration to a report on the activities of the Jewish Self-Administration for 1942, drawn up for the SS headquarters
APT A 7857

(97) A book of surgical operations performed in the Ghetto
APT A 9150, k. 41/Sb. poz., s. 77, Photo: M. Posselt

(98) A. Bergel: Library in the Ghetto, November 27, 1943
BR: 27. XI.43 / Bergel
collotype, ozalid, paper, 295 x 212, Heřman collection, PT 4285

(99) A souvenir poster for a performance of Verdi's Requiem rehearsed by R. Schächter
paper, 300 x 210, Heřman collection, PT 4296

(100) A selection of drawings and documents on display on a round panel from an extensive corpus of documentation collected by K. Heřman
Photo: M. Posselt

(101) A souvenir poster for the celebration of the feast of Hanukkah in 1943
paper, 300 x 210, Heřman collection, PT 3917

(102) A souvenir poster for Gogol's play Ženitba
India ink drawing, watercolor, pencil, pastel, paper, 296 x 210, Heřman collection, PT 4302

(103) A souvenir poster for the play Der Erfolg des Kolumbus
pen and India ink drawing, pastel, paper, 300 x 210, Heřman collection, PT 4030

(104) A souvenir poster for the cabaret Karussel
CL: Holland
pen and India ink drawing, watercolor, paper, 300 x 210, Heřman collection, PT 4293

(105) A souvenir poster for the cabaret Ať žije život
watercolor, pencil and crayon drawing, paper, 300 x 210, Heřman collection, PT 3893

(106) Leo Haas: Cabaret in a yard
BL: Terezín, Kabaret, BR: Leo Haas
India ink wash drawing, paper, 410 x 501, PT 1884

(107) Tickets for a cultural performance in the Ghetto
APT A 1260-2a, A 1260-2b, A 1260-2c, A 1260-3a, A 1260-3b, A 1260-6, A 11843

(108) Photograph of R. Feder, the rabbi of Kolín
JMP 46527

(109) Manuscript of a Jewish prayer from the Terezín Ghetto
Photocopy, APT 9329

(110) A mezuzah (a case with a Jewish prayer) from the Terezín Ghetto
PT 414, Photo: M. Posselt

(111) Figurine of a rabbi
PT 8876, Photo: M. Posselt

(112) F. Bloch: Services in the loft
BR: feb
colored pen and India ink drawing, paper, 201 x 214, JMP 173052/3, © Jewish Museum in Prague

(113) Photograph of E. Redlich as a student
FAPT 1495

(114) Part of the Ak/St transport list with E. Redlich's name
APT A 7344

(115) Redlich's diary with a bag in which it was hidden
APT A 1226/2-1

(116) Old Jews in the German town of Hanau before boarding a transport train
BPK – NS 793

(117) Contract on the "purchase of home"
APT A 49/89 k. 13/KT, s. 87

(118) K. Fleischmann: Elderly women waiting for food, 1942
BR: KF 42
pencil drawing, paper, 207 x 178, JMP 176772, © Jewish Museum in Prague

(119) K. Fleischmann: An elderly woman lying down
pastel, paper, 300 x 215, PT 13136

(120) Photograph of V. Eisinger
FAPT 1523

(121) Photograph of F. Dicker-Brandeisová
JMP, Sb. fot. VI/34, č. neg. 26683

(122) Records of the Youth Care Department of the Jewish Self-Administration on the number of children in the Ghetto as of September 12, 1943
JMP, T, i. č. 300

(123) A teaching aid used in the Ghetto for teaching Hebrew
JMP, T, i. č. 310

(124) Cover page of the primer "Poupata" used in Czech schools
APT A 7171

(125) A souvenir poster for the performance of the play Broučci
BR: Pöck
watercolor, carton, 295 x 210, Heřman collection, PT 4299

(126) Performance of the children's opera Brundibár in a picture from a Nazi propaganda documentary
NFA – FAPT A 1890

(127) Cover page of the magazine "Domov"
Magazine "Domov", issue No. I a, December 30, 1943, APT A 11 461, K 49
Sb. poz.

(128) Phototograph of Jews assembled before their departure for a transport train (picture from Plzeň)
Západočeské muzeum v Plzni, národopisné oddělení, II/2b

(129) Photograph of the concentration camp Westerbork
NIOD 57 C 25576/12

(130) Photograph of Slovak Jews on their way to a transport
JMP, Sb. fot., IV/13, č. neg. 20861

(131) Index cards of Danish Jews from the Terezín Ghetto
APT, PM A 2/93, k 10/Gh.

(132) A secret message smuggled out of the Ghetto
APT A 313/1

(133) A postcard sent from the Ghetto
APT A 9310

(134) A dispatch note and label on one of the International Red Cross consignments sent to the Terezín Ghetto
APT A 3671 / K 16 / Gh

(135) Wire from the Auschwitz Camp Command on V. Lederer's escape
APMO D-Aul-1/1a, tom 3, s. 358

(136) A false identification card used by the former Terezín prisoner V. Lederer after his escape from Auschwitz
FAPT 1492

(137) Photograph of a heap of human remains at Majdanek
ČTK 285 295/1

(138) Photograph of the arrival of Jewish prisoners on the site of their labor assignment in Riga
BPK – W II 164

(139) Photograph of the members of a death squad (Einsatzkommando)
taken from: Martin Gilbert, The Dent Atlas of the Holocaust. The Complete History, Oxford 1993, p. 65

(140) Photograph of a street in the Lublin Ghetto
BPK – W II 19b

(141) Photograph of a mobile gas chamber
taken from: S. Zeitun, D. Foucher, Résistance et deportation, Lyon 1997, p. 176

(142) Photograph of the victims of a mass execution of Jews in Estonia, dead bodies ready for burning
ČTK 256 961/2

(143) Photograph of the arrival of a transport in the Kulmhof camp
JMP, Sb. fot. IV/16, č. neg. 21192

(144) Photograph of R. Masárek
FAPT 5246

(145) An aerial photo of the Sobibór extermination camp
Muzeum byłego hitlerowskiego obozu zagłady w Sobiborze, Sobibór

(146) Photograph of the railway station building at Treblinka
BPK – NS 852

(147) The Auschwitz camp complex in an aerial picture taken by the US Air Force on June 26, 1944
BPK – NS 822

(148) Photograph of a "selection" in the camp Auschwitz II - Birkenau
YV FA – 268/25

(149) Plan of sector BIIb of the Birkenau camp where the "Terezín family camp" was located
APT A 65/89

(150) Photograph of one of the barracks in the "family camp"
APMO – B Nr. neg. fot. 3590

(151) Photograph of the building of crematorium No. 2 in Auschwitz
APMO Nr. neg. fot. 20 995/506

(152) Photograph of the building of crematorium No. 3 in Auschwitz
APMO Nr. neg. fot. 20 995/488

(153) O. Sgall's letter from Auschwitz
APT A 38/89

(154) Photograph taken from the arrival ramp at Birkenau towards the site where the "family camp" used to stand
FAPT 5547/21

(155) Photograph of a cement works at Golleschau (Goleszów)
APMO Nr. neg. fot. 16564

(156) Photograph of a plant producing synthetic petrol at Blechhammer (Blachownia Śląska)
APMO Nr. neg. fot. 10767

(157) Photograph of bombed-out Hamburg
FAPT 971

(158) Photograph of the concentration camp Stutthof (Sztutowo)
taken from: Arbeitsmappe Polen – Hrsg. Aktion Sühnezeichen/Friedensdienste e. V.

(159) Part of the list of prisoners from Kaufering
JMP, DP, i. č. 62/4

(160) Photograph of the branch of the Mauthausen concentration camp at Gusen
FAPT 1340

(161) Photograph of the burial of victims into a mass grave at Bergen-Belsen after the camp's liberation
BPK – NS 828

(162) Photograph of an evacuation transport passing through the Velim railway station
SÚA, KPSVZ, k. 66, s. 305

(163) Photograph of the ruins of the gas chamber in crematorium No. 2 in Auschwitz
FAPT 5547/4

(164) Photograph of the exhumation of a mass grave containing the victims of death march from Schwarzheide to Terezín
FAPT A 5175

(165) Lobby of the Ghetto Museum
Photo: M. Posselt

(166) Scale model of the Terezín Ghetto in the lobby of the Museum
Photo: M. Posselt

(167) The Museum's cinema hall
Photo: M. Posselt

(168) The study room in the Museum
Photo: M. Posselt

TEREZÍN IN THE "FINAL SOLUTION OF THE JEWISH QUESTION" 1941–1945

Guide to the Permanent Exhibition of the Ghetto Museum in Terezín

Text written by Vojtěch Blodig.

Photos, pictorial materials, plans and texts were provided by the Terezín Memorial; the Jewish Museum in Prague; the Czech Press Agency in Prague; the National Film Archives in Prague; the State Central Archives in Prague; the West Bohemian Museum in Plzeň; Archiwum Państwowego Muzeum Auschwitz-Birkenau w Oświęcimiu, Oświęcim; Muzeum byłego hitlerowskiego obozu zagłady w Sobiborze, Sobibór; Bildarchiv Preussischer Kulturbesitz, Berlin; Yad Vashem Film&Photo Archive, Jerusalem; Comité international de la Croix-Rouge, Genève; Nederlands Instituut voor Oorlogsdocumentatie, Amsterdam; Helga Hošková; publishing houses given in the list of reproduced exhibits; Milan Posselt; Miroslav Veselý (pages 126–127, 129); Milan Ressel and Jana Nováková.

Translated by Jan Valeška; Lewis Paines.

Graphic layout and cover design by Petr Osvald.

Published in 2003, 2006 by Helena Osvaldová, Nakladatelství OSWALD, Prague (www.oswald.eu) for Terezín Memorial, Principova alej 304, CZ-411 55 Terezín (www.pamatnik-terezin.cz).

First edition.
Prague 2003, 2006.

ISBN 80-85433-89-3 (English version)
ISBN 80-85433-88-5 (Czech version)
ISBN 80-85433-90-7 (German version)
ISBN 80-85433-91-5 (Hebrew version)